Biotechnology

With Student Activities

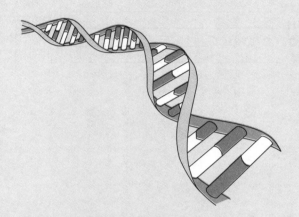

Laura M. Johnson
Middle School Science Teacher
Revere Public Schools
Revere, MA

Amsco School Publications, Inc.
315 Hudson Street, New York, N.Y. 10013

The publisher wishes to acknowledge the helpful contributions
of the following reviewers in the preparation of this book:

Vanessa Brunet
Biology Teacher
Oak Hill High School
Hineston, Louisiana

Daniel L. Sitzman
Curriculum Specialist
Omaha North High Magnet School
Omaha, Nebraska

Rhonda Creed-Harry
Math and Science Educator
Harlem Renaissance High School
New York, New York

LeeAnn Vaughan
High School Science Educator
Omaha Public Schools
Omaha, Nebraska

Cover Photo: Genetic engineering montage showing chromosomes, DNA, chemicals,
a sheep, and cloning © Fotosearch/Image Zoo Illustrations.
Cover Design: Meghan J. Shupe
Composition: Dan Kantor/Sierra Graphics
Text Design: Howard Petlack/A Good Thing, Inc.
Artwork: Hadel Studio

Please visit our Web site at: *www.amscopub.com*

When ordering this book, please specify:
either **R 176 W** or BIOTECHNOLOGY: WITH STUDENT ACTIVITIES

ISBN13: 978-1-56765-948-1 / NYC Item: 1-56765-948-0

Contents

To the Student

This book has been written to introduce you to the exciting field of biotechnology. You may have heard about recent advances in genetic engineering, biofuels, and stem cell research; these are all part of the world of biotechnology. With the knowledge you gain from this book, you will better understand how and why biotechnology is such an important part of your life. The text discusses biotechnology topics in a balanced manner, so that both sides of an issue are covered. In this way, you will be better able to form your own opinions on the various uses of biotechnology in society.

In addition to numbered lessons, each chapter contains several hands-on activities, such as Student Mini-Labs, Graphing Skills, and Student Activities. These creative assignments are related to the topics covered in the lessons and offer you the opportunity to work on your own, in pairs, or in teams. The lessons and activities often include sections that you will need to complete, such as tables, charts, diagrams, and fill-in questions. Since you are not permitted to write in the book, you (or your teacher) will have to print out these pages. A small image of a CD labeled "Print This" will appear at the start of such activities. The CD attached to the inside back cover of this book contains the entire text, including these activities. Your teacher will let you know when you have to print out the pages needed to complete an assignment.

We hope that you will find this book both informative and enjoyable.

To the Teacher

The aim of this book is to introduce students to the rapidly growing field of biotechnology—from the first applications thousands of years ago, to the advances in genetic engineering and stem cell research that have been made in the past few decades. With that knowledge, students may better understand how and why biotechnology is becoming such an integral part of their lives. Students particularly need this information because many of these topics have become hotly debated issues. The text approaches controversial topics in a neutral manner, so that both the positive and the negative aspects are discussed. Students in middle school are at the age where they can begin to think abstractly; this book will help them reflect upon their views of biotechnology so that they may form their own opinions. *Biotechnology* has been written with the idea of Differentiated Instruction (DI) in mind; it can be taught to middle-school students of different learning abilities, as well as to high-school life science or biology students as supplementary material. The DI provided by this book may benefit ELL students who are first learning English, students on Individualized Education Programs (IEP), mainstream (on-level) students, and/or higher-achieving Honors students.

The text is written in a user-friendly manner that is easy to understand. It consists of six chapters, each divided into several numbered lessons. Each chapter opens with a photograph related to one of the topics covered and an Essential Question to focus students on the chapter's main idea. The lesson titles are phrased as questions to help engage students' interest and focus their reading. Individual lessons may be taught over a few days or longer, depending on the needs of your students. Lessons include abundant figures and photographs to help elucidate the concepts being taught. Each lesson is followed by a complete set of questions (vocabulary, multiple-choice, true-false, and short answer) to help students review the topics and assess their comprehension of the material. For more advanced students, Going Further questions (often designed for Internet research) are included to offer more challenging work.

In addition to the lessons, each chapter includes several of the following activities: Student Mini-Labs; Graphing Skills; and Student Activities. These creative, hands-on activities enrich and extend the topics covered and offer students the opportunity to work on their own, in pairs, or in teams to complete the assignments. The lessons and activities often include connections to other disciplines (such as math and social studies), further reinforcing the relevance of biotechnology to the students' lives. At the end of every chapter is a complete set of review questions, including a crossword puzzle that uses all the vocabulary terms covered in that chapter. (*Note*: All vocabulary words appear in boldfaced type when first introduced; other important terms are italicized for emphasis.)

This book can be used to teach biotechnology in many ways, including: as the *main source* of textual information in a biotechnology class (i.e., forming the curriculum); as *supplementary material* for a regular life science class, when the teacher wants to incorporate biotechnology topics into the curriculum (such as genetic engineering, cloning, and stem cells); and as *a review* of specific life science topics, particularly those covered in Chapter 3 (DNA: Purpose, Structure, and Function) and Chapter 4 (Mutations and Genetic Diseases). As such, it could be used to review specific topics at the end of the year in a life science class or to review some life science topics before a state-mandated proficiency test.

A complete biotechnology class could also be taught as an elective; this would be in addition to the students' regular life science class. This book can be used for either of the following course formats: classes held every day for *one* full semester for mainstream and other students; or classes held every day for *two* semesters for Honors students (as their in-depth assignments and activities often take more time to complete).

We hope that you and your students will find this book enjoyable as well as educational.

Introduction to Biotechnology

Essential Question:
What are some of the first ways that people used living things to improve their lives?

Contents

Warm-Up Activity

What do you think you already know about the science called **biotechnology**? Write at least one word or phrase for each letter in the word below that you think describes something about biotechnology. The letter may begin the word you choose or it may appear in the middle or end of the word. For example, if you choose the word *science*, the letters "sc" could go before the letter "i" and the letters "ence" would follow after. Other examples are also shown.

B
ScIence
O
BacTeria
E
Stem Cells
H
N
BiOlogy
L
ClOnes
G
Genes
Y

At this point you might ask: "What exactly does *biotechnology* mean?" and "What does it have to do with me?" Good questions! This chapter will help you define biotechnology and show you the many different ways that biotechnology affects your life. Have you ever eaten bread and cheese; taken the medicine penicillin; or owned a dog? Have you ever wondered how people clean up oil spills or make an alternative fuel from corn? Did you ever wonder how scientists find cures for some of the diseases that people are born with? Or have you ever heard news reports about people cloning animals or using stem cells to try to treat diseases? All of these processes involve biotechnology!

The word *biotechnology* can be broken into two parts: *bio-* is a prefix (a word part that is attached in front of a word) that means "life" or "living things"; *technology* refers to the use of specific knowledge to change or develop processes and items that benefit people. So, when we combine the two, we get our definition of biotechnology: It is the practical use of new procedures and devices based on discoveries about living things (biology).

biotechnology

"life or living things"

"practical use of knowedge"

Here are two other ways to define biotechnology:

➡ Biotechnology is a science that uses living things (or parts of them, such as genes) to change other living things to make products for human use.
➡ A simpler definition is that biotechnology is the science of using or changing living things to improve or benefit people's lives.

In both of these definitions you see the term *living things*. Throughout this book, you will often see the word *organism* used instead of "living things." An **organism** is a more scientific word used to refer to any living thing. A tree is an organism. A fish is an organism. *You* are an organism. You will also be reading about very small living things. These things are so small that you can see them only by viewing through a microscope. These very small living things are called **microorganisms** (the prefix *micro-* means "very small"). Some examples of the microorganisms that

you will be reading about in this chapter are bacteria and yeast. (See Figure 1-1.)

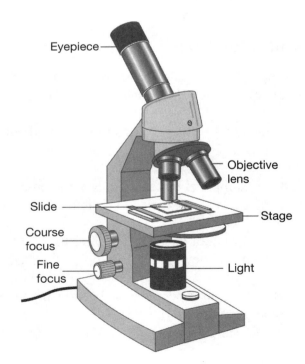

Figure 1-1. A microscope is used for viewing tiny organisms.

Labels on figure: Eyepiece, Objective lens, Slide, Stage, Course focus, Fine focus, Light

You will read about many different examples of biotechnology in this book. All of these examples show how people use other living things to improve the quality of human life. In fact, you will learn that people have been using processes that could be considered forms of "biotechnology" for thousands of years. Although the word *biotechnology* was first used in the 1940s, it has been within the past 25 years that scientists have made the greatest advances in the field. For example, biotechnology researchers have figured out how to: change the DNA of organisms (the process called *genetic engineering*); make a complete copy of an organism (the process called *cloning*); and use a special type of cell to try to cure certain diseases (by a process that uses *stem cells*). Before you read about these more recent discoveries, you will learn about the first ways in which people used different organisms to help them live better lives.

Lesson 1.1 Review

Vocabulary Check

For each of the following terms, give a complete definition.

1. Biotechnology

2. Organism

3. Microorganism

Multiple Choice

For each question, choose the letter of the answer choice that best completes the sentence or answers the question.

1. Which of the following is a product made by biotechnology?
   a. bread   b. cheese   c. penicillin   d. all of these

2. One example of biotechnology is the process of making fuel from
   a. oil spills   b. corn   c. stem cells   d. cheese

3. The word part, or prefix, *bio* refers to
   a. technical devices   b. people   c. useful items   d. living things

4. How long have people have been using processes that are considered forms of biotechnology?
   a. thousands of years   b. 1000 years   c. 150 years   d. 20 years

5. The word *biotechnology* has been in use since the
   a. 1700s   b. 1800s   c. 1900s   d. 2000s

True or False

Read each statement and indicate whether it is true or false. If it is false, correct the underlined word(s) to make the statement true.

1. Technology means something that <u>helps</u> us.

1. _____

2. A tree <u>is not</u> an organism.

2. _____

3. Microorganisms can only be seen with a <u>microscope</u>.

3. _____

4. The prefix micro means <u>very large</u>.

4. _____

5. Within the past <u>75</u> years, scientists have made the greatest advances in biotechnology.

5. _____

Short Answer

Answer the following questions in one or two complete sentences.

1. What is the term for word parts such as "bio" and "micro"?
2. Define "biotechnology" using the word *organism* in your answer.
3. Compare and contrast: (a) how organisms and microorganisms are similar; and (b) how organisms and microorganisms are different.
4. What are some of the developments in biotechnology that have been made in the past 25 years?

Going Further

With a partner from class, do research on the Internet to identify at least five processes or products of biotechnology (*not* already covered in this lesson) that benefit you in your daily life.

How Did the Process of Cheese-Making Start?

One of the earliest examples of how people used a living thing to help them was in the process of making cheese. Since the development of cheese happened so long ago, no one is really sure how it came to be. However, some scientists, called *archaeologists*, who study past civilizations by looking at the remains of their objects, or *artifacts*, think that it was probably discovered by accident about 6000 years ago. This most likely occurred in the Middle East, when people did not have many of the materials that we have today. They used the resources available to them, most of which came from animals. So, when traveling, people would sometimes carry their belongings in sacks made from animal stomachs.

Archaeologists think that cheese was discovered in ancient times when people, who transported their milk in sacks made from young animals' stomachs, noticed that the milk was forming small edible lumps. These lumps, called curds, are the substances that turn into cheese. The curds were formed due to an enzyme that lined the sacks. An **enzyme** is a protein found in organisms that can have an effect on chemical reactions. The enzyme from the lining of the stomachs that was turning the milk into cheese is called **rennin**, which is extracted from a substance called *rennet*. Rennet is found in the stomachs of young calves and other milk-drinking domestic animals.

While cheese-making is a similar process today, there are two main differences. First, the milk is now heated to kill harmful microorganisms before it is turned into cheese (a process called *pasteurization*). Second, the en-

Figure 1-2. **A type of bacterium called P. shermanii gives Swiss cheese its distinct appearance.**

zyme rennin is still used in cheese-making, but it must be intentionally added to the milk. In most places nowadays, milk is stored in huge tanks (rather than in small stomach sacks), so the enzyme that makes cheese from milk has to be added.

When the rennin is added, it makes the proteins in the liquid milk stick together and form clumps called curds. These curds are then separated from the rest of the liquid, which is called *whey*. After that, various salts and bacteria are added to create the many different types and flavors of cheese. **Bacteria** are microorganisms that have only one cell. Different bacteria will produce different types of cheese. For example, to create Swiss cheese, a type of bacterium called *P. shermanii* is added, which creates gas bubbles in the cheese. These gas bubbles then leave the holes in the cheese, giving Swiss cheese its distinct appearance. (See Figure 1-2.)

Cheese-making is an example of biotechnology because people used a substance from a living thing (rennin from the lining of an animal's stomach) to help them make another product; that is, to make cheese from the milk of domesticated animals. Making cheese was a great advantage to people when it was first discovered thousands of years ago; the cheese stayed fresh longer, and was easier to transport, than milk. (Remember, they did not have refrigerators to help preserve food in those days.) Cheese is still important today for its nutritional value and its many uses in our foods.

Vocabulary Check

For each of the following terms, give a complete definition.

1. Enzyme

2. Rennin

3. Bacteria

Multiple Choice

For each question, choose the letter of the answer choice that best completes the sentence or answers the question.

1. The process of cheese-making probably started about how many years ago?
   a. 60   b. 100   c. 600   d. 6000

2. In ancient times, sacks for carrying milk were made from
   a. canvas   b. animal stomachs   c. nylon   d. plastic

3. Adding a certain enzyme to milk makes clumps called
   a. curds   b. proteins   c. whey   d. butter

4. The name of the enzyme that turns the milk into cheese is
   a. *P. shermanii*   b. rennet   c. rennin   d. milk

True or False

Read each statement and indicate whether it is true or false. If it is false, correct the underlined word(s) to make the statement true.

1. A substance called <u>rennet</u> contains the enzyme that turns the milk into cheese.

   1. _____

2. Rennet is a substance found in the stomachs of <u>milk-drinking animals</u>.

   2. _____

3. Rennin <u>is not still</u> used today to turn milk into cheese.

   3. _____

4. Milk is now <u>heated before</u> it is turned into cheese, in order to kill harmful bacteria.

   4. _____

5. <u>Enzymes</u> are used to create the different types and flavors of cheese.

   5. _____

Short Answer

Answer the following questions in one or two complete sentences.

1. Give an educated guess as to why no one is *exactly* sure how cheese was first developed.
2. How do scientists think cheese was developed thousands of years ago?
3. Explain how bacteria are involved in the creation of Swiss cheese.
4. Explain why cheese-making is an example of biotechnology.
5. Give two reasons why turning milk into cheese was helpful for people living thousands of years ago.

Going Further

Imagine that you are a person living in the Middle East in 4000 B.C. and that you recently discovered how to make a new food when you carried milk inside animal stomachs. Write a letter to a friend who lives in another city explaining what has happened and what you do with this new food.

Lesson 1.3 — Did People First Bake Bread by Accident?

Another example of an early type of biotechnology is the process of bread-making. As with the development of cheese, no one is exactly sure how bread was first made. It is known that bread has been around for thousands of years, so its introduction happened long before events were written down. Archaeologists have had to make an educated guess as to how ancient peoples came to make bread. It is thought that, like cheese, early bread was developed by accident, and that this may have happened in the Middle East (Mesopotamia and Egypt) about 6000 years ago.

Archaeologists think that before bread was developed, wild grains were crushed into a substance called *flour*, which was mixed with water to create a type of dough. This dough was baked into flatbreads over fires or hot stones. These flatbreads did not look like most of the bread we eat today. The wheat in the bread also changed over time; as ancient people grew it, the wheat became less like the original wild grain and more like the grain we now have. (See Figures 1-3a and b.)

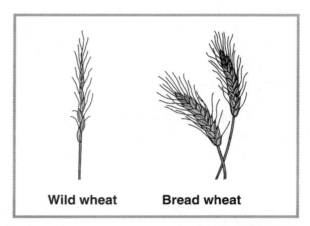

Wild wheat   **Bread wheat**

Figure 1-3b. The wheat plant has changed over time as people selected for larger kernels.

This microorganism is a type of *fungus* (which is neither a plant nor an animal) and it is called **yeast**. This fungus is found naturally in the air and in the ground. Archaeologists propose that when the dough was left outside long enough, some yeast that was in the air accidentally landed on the dough, which caused the dough to rise and form bread. Since then, yeast has been used by people all over the world to make breads rise.

Like all other living things, yeast needs nutrients and produces a waste product. In this case, the yeast gets its nutrients when it

Figure 1-3a. Dough from grain has been baked into flatbreads for many centuries.

Bread, as we now know it, results from the effect that a tiny organism has on the dough.

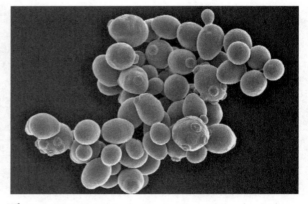

Figure 1-4. The kind of yeast used for bread-making is *S. cerevisiae*, commonly called baker's yeast.

eats the sugars in the flour; and it produces carbon-dioxide gas as a waste. This process is called **fermentation**. When gas bubbles form throughout the dough, the whole dough rises, producing the bread that we are familiar with today. Although there are many species of yeast, the specific kind of yeast that is used today is *S. cerevisiae*, commonly referred to as baker's yeast. (See Figure 1-4.)

Bread-making is an example of biotechnology because a living thing (the microorganism yeast) is used to help humans by turning flour and water into bread. Clearly, bread is an important part of our lives. We may use different types of bread to make toast, sandwiches, dessert breads, bread crumbs for stuffing, and even croutons for salads. Just as people have been doing for thousands of years, bakers also experiment with creating different types of breads by adding various ingredients such as fruit, honey, spices, and nuts. Had ancient people not discovered how yeast could make their bread rise thousands of years ago, we may never have developed such an important part of our lives.

Lesson 1.3 Review

Vocabulary Check

For each of the following terms, give a complete definition.

1. Yeast

2. Fermentation

Multiple Choice

For each question, choose the letter of the answer choice that best completes the sentence or answers the question.

1. Bread-making was probably developed in
   a. Egypt and Mesopotamia   b. South Africa   c. China   d. Australia

2. The discovery of bread probably occurred how many years ago?
   a. 2000   b. 4000   c. 6000   d. 10,000

3. The substance that makes bread dough rise is called
   a. bacteria   b. grains   c. yeast   d. flour

4. The species of yeast that is commonly referred to as baker's yeast is named
   a. *S. cerevisiae*   b. *E. coli*   c. *P. shermanii*   d. *B. yeastisiae*

True or False

Read each statement and indicate whether it is true or false. If it is false, correct the underlined word(s) to make the statement true.

1. Bread was probably developed <u>on purpose</u>.

2. Before bread was developed, ground grains and water were baked over fires to produce <u>flatbreads</u>.

3. Yeast is found <u>only in the ground</u>.

4. The process that makes bread rise is called <u>fermentation</u>.

5. The substance that causes bubbles to form in the dough is <u>hydrogen gas</u>.

1. _____

2. _____

3. _____

4. _____

5. _____

Short Answer

Answer the following questions in one or two complete sentences.

1. Describe how archaeologists think bread was developed.
2. How is yeast like all other living things?
3. Explain how the activity of yeast causes dough to rise.
4. Explain why bread-making is an example of biotechnology.

Going Further

Louis Pasteur was a nineteenth-century French chemist who made many important contributions to science, including our understanding of the fermentation process. Either on your own or with a partner research on the Internet the life and scientific work of Louis Pasteur; write a one-page report.

   In your report, include what Pasteur discovered about fermentation. Remember to properly cite the sources you used to find your information. Your essay will be graded according to the rubric given by your teacher. If you are working with a partner, you may want to split up different topics to research, and edit each other's work before combining the two parts into your one-page report.

How Was Penicillin's Special Property Discovered?

If you have ever been sick with an ear or respiratory infection, a doctor may have prescribed an antibiotic to help you get better. An **antibiotic** is a substance that kills the bacteria that can make people sick. (The prefix *anti-* means "against"; you have already learned that *bio-* means "living things.") While you might take this medicine for granted, there was a time—less than only 100 years ago—when a simple infection could kill a person because doctors had no treatment for it. That is, until a discovery occurred one summer day at a laboratory in England.

In 1928, a British scientist named Dr. Alexander Fleming made a very important, yet accidental, discovery that forever changed our lives. Fleming had been studying bacteria. That summer, before he left for a vacation, Fleming left some petri dishes filled with samples of bacteria out on his workbench. When he returned, he examined the samples and noticed something very peculiar in one of the dishes. Fleming observed that a type of mold called *Penicillium notatum* had landed in the dish and that there were no bacteria growing around it. A **mold** is a microorganism that, like yeast, is a type of fungus. The mold is usually black, blue, or green; it gets its nutrients by absorbing them from other organisms. The mold may have come in through an open window or through air vents. Fleming realized the great potential of a substance that could prevent the growth of bacteria, but he could

not extract enough of it from the mold to use in his own experiments. He published his findings, and then moved on to other research. (See Figure 1-5.)

It was not until 1939 that two scientists working together in England were able to extract the bacteria-killing substance from the mold. Dr. Howard Florey and Dr. Ernst Chain, along with their research team, knew that the mold Fleming was working with had antibiotic properties. Fortunately, they were able to extract enough of the special substance that was responsible for killing bacteria. They called that substance with medicinal properties **penicillin**.

Once they had a big enough sample of the penicillin, Florey and Chain needed to test it on mice before they could consider giving it to people. This is a common practice when scientists first develop a medicine because they want to make sure that the medicine is both safe and effective. To do their experiment, the doctors injected eight mice with a type of bacteria called *Streptococcus*. Then they injected four of the eight mice with penicillin and left the other four untreated. The following day, the four mice treated with penicillin were alive and no longer had a bacterial infection. However, the four mice that did not get the penicillin did not survive. This experiment demonstrated the potential medicinal value of penicillin. The scientists theorized that penicillin could be used to cure bacterial infections in people.

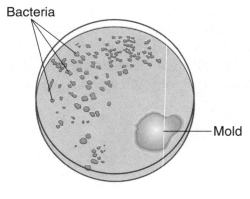

Bacteria

Mold

Figure 1-5. Fleming observed that there were no bacteria growing around a mold called *Penicillium notatum*, which had landed in the lab dish.

Before giving penicillin to the masses, the scientists first had to test the medicine on a few people. Their first attempt was in 1941 on a policeman who had developed a bad infection as a result of a scratch on his skin. He did show some signs of improving but, unfortunately, they did not have enough of the drug to save him. The scientists then tried penicillin on some sick children, because they had only a small amount of penicillin; because they are smaller, children do not need as much of a dose of medicine as adults do. Thankfully, the experiment was a success and all of the children recovered from their infections. After this, penicillin was used in World War II for people fighting in the war. It saved the lives of many who would have otherwise died from infections.

After World War II, Drs. Chain and Florey went to the United States to work on ways to produce penicillin in huge amounts and sell it. They worked with drug companies and eventually found better ways of extracting penicillin from the mold. Eventually, penicillin became available to everyone. All three scientists who contributed to the discovery of penicillin (Dr. Fleming, Dr. Florey, and Dr. Chain) were awarded the Nobel Prize in Medicine in 1945. The development of penicillin is considered an example of biotechnology because part of a living thing (an extract from a mold) was used to help cure people of their bacterial infections. Penicillin has saved the lives of many people (and animals), and because of this it is sometimes referred to as a "wonder drug."

Lesson 1.4 Review

Vocabulary Check

For each of the following terms, give a complete definition.

1. Antibiotic

2. Mold

3. Penicillin

Multiple Choice

For each question, choose the letter of the answer choice that best completes the sentence or answers the question.

1. Dr. Fleming discovered penicillin in the year
   a. 1928   b. 1939   c. 1941   d. 1945

2. The species of microorganism that landed in Dr. Fleming's petri dish was
   a. *Streptococcus*   b. *Penicillium notatum*   c. *P. shermanii*   d. *S. cerevisiae*

3. Penicillin comes from the type of organism that is called a
  a. plant   b. mold   c. mammal   d. bacterium

4. In the experiment on mice, Dr. Florey and Dr. Chain gave how many mice the injections of penicillin?
  a. zero   b. four   c. six   d. eight

True or False

Read each statement and indicate whether it is true or false. If it is false, correct the underlined word(s) to make the statement true.

1. In the word *antibiotic*, the prefix "anti-" means <u>for</u>.   1. _____

2. Before penicillin, bacterial infections <u>were never</u> deadly.   2. _____

3. Dr. Fleming's discovery was <u>an accident</u>.   3. _____

4. In Florey's and Chain's experiment on mice, <u>none</u> of the mice that were given penicillin lived.   4. _____

5. In the first attempt at giving penicillin to cure a person, the policeman <u>lived</u>.   5. _____

6. For their work, all three scientists involved in the discovery of penicillin were awarded the <u>Nobel Prize in Medicine</u>.   6. _____

Short Answer

Answer the following questions in one or two complete sentences.

1. Why did Dr. Fleming suspect that there was something about the mold *Penicillium notatum* that could kill bacteria?
2. Briefly describe how Dr. Florey and Dr. Chain tested penicillin on mice.
3. In the experiment on mice, why did the researchers give only half of the mice injections of penicillin and leave the other half untreated?
4. What were the results of the experiment on the mice?
5. Why did the penicillin work on the sick children but *not* on the sick policeman?
6. Why is the development of penicillin an example of biotechnology?

Going Further

Think about Dr. Florey's and Dr. Chain's experiment in which they tested the effects of penicillin on mice. Do you think it was okay that they performed this experiment using live mice? In a two-paragraph response, discuss at least two pros (positive things) and two cons (negative things) about using lab mice for scientific experiments.

Lesson 1.5 — Is Selective Breeding a Form of Biotechnology?

Have you ever looked at all the different types of dogs and been amazed by the variety? Dogs are one of the most varied mammal species, with at least 400 different types, or *breeds*. From Poodles to Chihuahuas to Great Danes, all these types of dogs are very different, yet they are all the same species. How did we get so many varieties? The answer is *selective breeding*. **Selective breeding** is the process by which two organisms with desirable traits are mated, or *bred*, to produce offspring with those same desired traits. **Offspring** is a word that refers to the one or more organisms that are produced by reproduction. In humans, the offspring are babies. The offspring of two dogs are puppies. The offspring of two plants would be the seeds that can grow into new plants. (See Figure 1-6.)

Figure 1-6. Selective breeding by people for specific characteristics produces the particular breeds of dogs we have today, such as these Yorkshire terriers.

Selective breeding is nothing new. This technique of creating an ideal organism has been around for thousands of years; it started when farmers tried to grow the biggest and best types of plants and animals. For example, farmers noticed that if they used the seeds (kernels) from only the biggest corn plants, the corn produced from those seeds generally would also be big. Over time, when this process was repeated, larger varieties of corn were developed. People noticed the same process with animals. If shepherds bred together two animals that were the biggest of their kind, their offspring would usually be big, too. However, people also realized that if they bred animals that were too closely re-lated (a process called *inbreeding*), they could obtain offspring that had severe health prob-lems and/or deformities.

Early farmers and shepherds realized that plants and animals passed on some sort of information to their offspring that made the offspring resemble their parents. Although these people did not know it, what these organisms were passing on to their offspring were their **genes** (the instructions for all traits). In animals, these genes control both the physical and behavioral traits. **Physical traits** are how an organism looks (such as its size, shape, color of fur, and so on). **Behavioral traits** are how an organism acts (such as its aggressiveness, level of energy, hunting ability, type of movement, and so on).

Selective breeding is an example of biotechnology because people change an or-ganism, over time, in order to benefit their own needs in some way. For example, let us look at dogs. Thousands of years ago, people hunted for their food. They needed a dog that was very fast so that it could help them run down the animal they were trying to hunt. To create a type of dog that was very fast, those people chose to breed only the fastest dogs that they had with other fast dogs. This would help to ensure that the dogs' traits (that is, genes) that made them fast would be passed on to their offspring.

One of the oldest and fastest dog breeds, the Saluki, is an example of a breed that was created by people (in the Middle East) who selectively bred very fast dogs together over a long period of time.

You can see the effects of selective breeding in many other common organisms, for example, apples, potatoes, cows, and sheep. All of these life-forms now look very different from how they used to look thousands of years ago, as people actively selected for different traits, such as size, color, and taste. As a result, we now have many different varieties of plants and animals. (See Figure 1-7.)

As useful as selective breeding has been to creating ideal organisms for people, there are also some drawbacks:

➡ *It takes a very long time to create a new type/breed of an organism.* It can take many generations of breeding, and many years, to obtain offspring that have the desired traits.

➡ *Only organisms of the same species may be crossed.* If organisms of similar (but not the same) species are crossed, there is a big chance that they could produce an organism that is sterile (that is, unable to reproduce).

➡ *Crossing closely related organisms in the hope of passing on a desirable trait may pass on undesirable traits as well.* This can be seen in many "purebred" dogs, which are known for being susceptible to some genetic diseases.

Figure 1-7. Selective breeding for different traits, such as size, color, and taste, has produced many varieties of apples.

Vocabulary Check

For each of the following terms, give a complete definition.

1. Selective breeding

2. Offspring

3. Genes

4. Physical traits

5. Behavioral traits

Multiple Choice

For each question, choose the letter of the answer choice that best completes the sentence or answers the question.

1. There are at least how many different breeds of dogs?
   a. 40   b. 400   c. 1000   d. 4000

2. The offspring of a plant would be its
   a. puppies   b. seeds   c. babies   d. mold

3. The first people to use selective breeding of plants and animals were
   a. scientists   b. doctors   c. farmers   d. teachers

4. Which of these organisms has changed in appearance over time because of selective breeding?
   a. apples   b. corn   c. dogs   d. all of these

True or False

Read each statement and indicate whether it is true or false. If it is false, correct the underlined word(s) to make the statement true.

1. The Poodle, Chihuahua, and Great Dane <u>are not</u> in the same species.   1. _____

2. Selective breeding has been around for <u>thousands of years</u>.   2. _____

3. When selective breeding was first started, it was used to develop <u>smaller</u> plants and animals.   3. _____

4. Breeding closely related animals can create offspring with <u>no health</u> problems.

4. _____

5. The Saluki was selectively bred to be a <u>very slow</u> dog.

5. _____

6. It usually takes a <u>very short time</u> to create a new breed of organism.

6. _____

Short Answer

Answer the following questions in one or two complete sentences.

1. Describe how farmers would use selective breeding to create bigger plants.
2. Explain why selective breeding is an example of biotechnology.
3. How could a person use selective breeding to create a very fast breed of dog?
4. What are *three* drawbacks to the practice of selective breeding?

Going Further

Go to the following Web site:

http://www.pbs.org/wgbh/harvest/engineer/select.html

Compare what happens to the type of corn produced in each generation when (a) you keep selecting the *biggest* ears of corn for one crop; and (b) you keep selecting the *smallest* ears of corn for another crop. Explain why this happens.

What Do Yeast Like to Eat?

Background Information

Yeast is a microorganism that takes in carbohydrates for food and releases carbon dioxide gas as a waste product. The more carbohydrates a food has, the more the yeast has to "eat." This is the process called *fermentation*, and it is responsible for making dough rise and turn into bread. In this student mini-lab experiment, you will test four different substances to find out which one produces the most carbon dioxide gas and, therefore, is the substance that yeast "likes to eat" the most. If yeast does not like to eat that substance, there will be no carbon dioxide produced. First, you will mix the yeast with water to "activate" the yeast and to give it a suitable environment for fermentation.

Purpose

To find out which substances yeast like to eat the most for fermentation

Materials

4 grams of sugar, 4 grams of oil, 4 grams of flour, and 4 grams of salt
1 liter of fresh water, divided evenly into 5 glasses
5 packets of baker's yeast (species *S. cerevisiae*)
5 medium-sized plastic, sealable food-storage bags
1 marker and tape to label each of the plastic bags

Directions

1. Dissolve the 5 packets of yeast in fresh water—one packet per each glass.
2. Pour the water-yeast mixtures into the 5 bags—one per each bag.
3. Pour the sugar into one bag and seal it. Label it "Sugar and yeast."
4. Pour the oil into another bag and seal it. Label it "Oil and yeast."
5. Pour the flour into a third bag and seal it. Label it "Flour and yeast."
6. Pour the salt into the fourth bag and seal it. Label it "Salt and yeast."
7. Nothing extra will be added to the fifth bag; it will contain just yeast and water. Label that bag "Yeast only." (*Note:* This will be your *control.*)
8. Place each bag on a table and wait at least 2 hours. At that time, check to see which bag has the most gas in it; that is, has visibly expanded from the carbon dioxide gas that was produced. (You may also be able to leave the bags and check back during your next class.)

Hypothesis

A **hypothesis** is an educated prediction that can be tested in an experiment. Form a hypothesis about which substance you think the yeast will like the most (in other words, the substance that will produce the most carbon dioxide gas).

I think that _____ will be the substance that
produces the greatest amount of carbon dioxide gas, and therefore is the one that
yeast likes to eat the most.

Data

Following the format shown below, rank each of the substances from 1 to 5 in order of the one with the most carbon dioxide gas (1) to the one with the least carbon dioxide (5). If there is more than one substance that produces either no gas or an equal amount of gas, write them on the same line.

Substance Added to the Yeast and Water Mixture	Amount of Carbon Dioxide Gas
	1st place
	2nd place
	3rd place
	4th place
	5th place

Analysis Questions

1. Which substance produced the most carbon dioxide gas?
2. Why do you think the substance in 1st place beat the substance in 2nd place?
3. (a) Which substance, or substances, produced no carbon dioxide gas?
   (b) Why do you think those substances produced no carbon dioxide gas?
4. Why was one bag left with just yeast and water, with no other substances added?

Conclusion and Evaluation

1. What can you conclude about the substance that yeast likes to eat the most?
2. Was your hypothesis supported? (Say yes or no.)
3. Do the results surprise you? Explain why or why not.

Enrichment

Think of more questions that you would like to test. Either on your own or in a group, form a hypothesis and then develop an experiment that could test your hypothesis. Perform this experiment and write a lab report that explains your results. Your lab report should follow the standard lab report format: Problem, Hypothesis, Procedure, Data/Results, Analysis, and Conclusion.

The Effect of Penicillin on Mice

The following set of data is from a similar (but hypothetical) experiment of the effects of penicillin on mice, much like the experiment that Dr. Florey and Dr. Chain performed. Two groups of mice were both injected with a lethal amount of *Streptococcus* bacteria. One group was given penicillin, while the other group was not. Use these data to draw a bar graph of the results on graph paper. Remember to include a title for the graph and labels on your x-axis and y-axis. (The x-axis should be the hours after the start of the experiment and the y-axis should be the number of mice that are alive). Also, remember to include a legend/key showing which bars on your graph represent each group of mice.

Effect of Penicillin on Mice Infected with *Streptococcus* Bacteria		
Hours after the start of experiment	Number of mice alive that were <u>not</u> given penicillin	Number of mice alive that were given penicillin
0	10	10
2	10	10
4	9	10
6	7	10
8	7	10
10	4	10
12	3	10
14	1	10
16	0	10

After you have graphed the results, answer the following questions.

Questions

1. What is the *total* number of mice that were originally used in this experiment?
2. Of the group of mice that was given penicillin, how many mice were alive after 10 hours?
3. Of the group of mice that was *not* given penicillin, how many mice were still alive after 10 hours?
4. In the end (after 16 hours), how many mice were still alive that were given penicillin?
5. In the end, how many mice were still alive that were *not* given penicillin?
6. What does your bar graph show about the effectiveness of penicillin for killing deadly bacteria in mice?

Student Activity - Version A

Introduction: You are a dog breeder who is asked by a client to start a new breed of dog. Your client wants her dog to be unique and has asked you to create a special dog. You will use your knowledge of **selective breeding** to help make your client happy! (Remember, when two breeds combine, the offspring have genes from *both* parents. Your new breed should resemble both parents. Also remember that for this to become a true breed, the offspring will have to be bred with other dogs that have similar traits over many generations.)

How: You will start your job by researching various dog breeds that you think are interesting. Use the following Web site (or any other Web site your teacher gives you) to collect information about the different breeds.

http://animal.discovery.com/breedselector/dogselectorindex.do

On this Web site, you may search for dogs in one of two ways:

1. If you have certain *traits* in mind that you would like your new dog to have, answer the questions in the "Dog Breed Selector" section to see what types of dogs match those characteristics.

2. If you already have certain *breeds* in mind, simply locate them on the "Dog Breed List" on the Web site.

You will record the particular traits of each dog (both **physical traits** and **behavioral traits**) on the "Dog Breed Information Sheet." After you have collected information on a variety of dogs, you will write up a detailed description of what physical and behavioral traits your new breed of dog has, based on the genes it got from both of its parent dogs.

Follow the "Dog Breed Project Template" on page 27 when putting together your project. You need to include the following information in your project:

- Name of new dog breed
- Detailed picture of new breed
- Name of this particular dog (e.g., Snoopy, Max, etc.)
- Physical and behavioral traits of the first (parent) breed used to create your new breed
- Physical and behavioral traits of the second (parent) breed used to create your new breed
- Physical and behavioral traits of your new dog breed
- Summary of what selective breeding is and how it was used to create this new breed

Your project will be graded according to the rubric given.

Dog Breed Information Sheet

Print This

First Breed's Name: _____

Behavioral Traits:

Amount of

Energy: _____

Exercise needed: _____

Playfulness: _____

Affection: _____

Scale:
1 = not much
2 = a little bit/some
3 = a medium amount
4 = more than other dogs
5 = very much

Friendliness toward other dogs: _____

Friendliness toward other pets: _____

Friendliness toward strangers: _____

Ease of training: _____

Watchdog ability: _____

Protection ability: _____

Grooming needed: _____

Cold tolerance: _____

Heat tolerance: _____

Temperament/Disposition: _____

_____

_____

Physical Traits:

Avg. height (male) _____ in.

Avg. height (female) _____ in.

Avg. weight (male) _____ lbs.

Avg. weight (female) _____ lbs.

Form and Function: (how it looks)

_____

_____

_____

_____

_____

_____

Other interesting information:	Draw a sketch of the dog here:

Second Breed's Name: _____

Behavioral Traits:

Amount of

Energy: _____

Exercise needed: _____

Playfulness: _____

Affection: _____

Scale:
1 = not much
2 = a little bit/some
3 = a medium amount
4 = more than other dogs
5 = very much

Friendliness toward other dogs: _____

Friendliness toward other pets: _____

Friendliness toward strangers: _____

Ease of training: _____

Watchdog ability: _____

Protection ability: _____

Grooming needed: _____

Cold tolerance: _____

Heat tolerance: _____

Temperament/Disposition: _____

_____

_____

Physical Traits:

Avg. height (male) _____ in.

Avg. height (female) _____ in.

Avg. weight (male) _____ lbs.

Avg. weight (female) _____ lbs.

Form and Function: (how it looks)

_____

_____

_____

_____

_____

_____

Other interesting information:	Draw a sketch of the dog here:

Dog Breed Project Template

Name of new breed
(e.g., Puggle)

Picture of new breed
(This should take up most of the page and be very detailed)

Name of your dog
(e.g., Snoopy)

Cover page

"Physical Traits"

- Written description of physical traits of breed #1 (4 to 5 sentences)

- Written description of physical traits of breed #2 (4 to 5 sentences)

- Written description of physical traits of NEW breed (4 to 5 sentences), which should be a combination of *both* parent breeds

Page 2

"Behavioral Traits"

- Written description of behavioral traits of breed #1 (4 to 5 sentences)

- Written description of behavioral traits of breed #2 (4 to 5 sentences)

- Written description of behavioral traits of NEW breed (4 to 5 sentences), which should be a combination of *both* parent breeds

Page 3

Summary of Selective Breeding

- A 1-to-2 paragraph written explanation of what selective breeding is and how you used it to create your new breed

You are writing this so that your client (the person for whom you are creating this new breed) can know more about how you developed their new breed of dog (it can be in a letter format).

Page 4

Introduction: You are a dog breeder who is asked by a client to start a new breed of dog. Your client wants her dog to be unique and has asked you to create a special dog. You will use your knowledge of **selective breeding** to help make your client happy!

How: You will start your job by researching various dog breeds that you think are interesting. Use the following Web site (or any other Web site your teacher gives you) to collect information about the different breeds.

http://animal.discovery.com/breedselector/dogselectorindex.do

On this Web site, you may search for dogs in one of two ways:

1. If you have certain *traits* in mind that you would like your new dog to have, answer the questions in the "Dog Breed Selector" section to see what types of dogs match those characteristics.

2. If you already have certain *breeds* in mind, simply locate them on the "Dog Breed List" on the Web site.

You will use the information that you collected and entered on your "Dog Breed Information Sheet" to use selective breeding to create a new breed of dog. This new breed will be a *hybrid* (which means a "mix") of two different breeds.

➡ Do a rough draft first on a separate sheet of paper.
➡ Do your final draft on a clean sheet of paper.
➡ Your final draft will be graded according to the rubric given.

Directions:

1. Write the names of the two dog breeds used to create your new dog breed.

2. Include the name of your new breed; this should be a combination of the two parent breeds' names. For example, a pug + a beagle = a "puggle" and a Labrador retriever + a poodle = a Labradoodle.

3. Draw a *detailed* picture of your new dog breed. This illustration should combine the desirable physical traits of both parent dogs.

4. Come up with a personal name for your dog (e.g., Snoopy, Max, etc.).

5. Write *five physical traits* of your new breed.

6. Write *five behavioral traits* of your new breed.

⎫
⎬ Your new breed should have traits from *both* parent dogs.
⎭

Chapter 1 Review

Vocabulary Crossword

Directions: *Each clue below is a definition of one of the vocabulary words that you learned in this chapter. On a printout of this page provided by your teacher, write the word that matches each definition inside the numbered vertical or horizontal spaces. All the vocabulary words from Chapter 1 are used in this puzzle.*

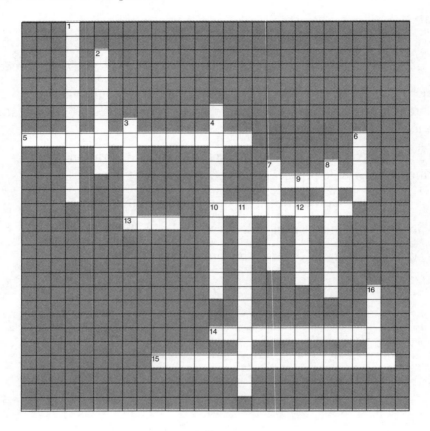

Across

5. How an organism acts (such as level of energy, aggressiveness, hunting ability, and so on)
9. Instructions for certain traits
10. An educated prediction that can be tested in an experiment
13. A microorganism that is a type of fungus, which is neither plant nor animal; usually black, blue, or green; gets its nutrients by absorbing them from other organisms
14. When yeast eats sugars and produces carbon dioxide gas
15. The process by which two organisms with desirable traits are mated together to produce offspring with those desired traits

Down

1. A very small living thing
2. The organism that is produced through reproduction
3. A living thing
4. The use of living things to help us improve our lives
6. A tiny, fungus microorganism that exists in the air and in the ground
7. Organisms that have only one cell; can be helpful and/or harmful
8. A substance that kills the bacteria that can make people sick
11. How an organism looks (such as shape, size, fur color, and so on)
12. A natural substance found in an organism that can affect chemical reactions
16. An enzyme from the lining of a mammal's stomach that can turn milk into cheese

Multiple Choice

For each question, choose the letter of the answer choice that best completes the sentence or answers the question.

1. The word *biotechnology* can be broken up into how many main word parts to help us understand it?
   a. two   b. three   c. four   d. six

2. Biotechnology means using or changing _____ to improve our lives.
   a. the environment   b. people   c. technology   d. living things

3. Archaeologists think that cheese was discovered about how many years ago?
   a. 8000   b. 7000   c. 6000   d. 5000

4. The substance that turns milk into cheese is a type of
   a. plant   b. fungus   c. enzyme   d. yeast

5. Which substance is found in the stomachs of milk-drinking animals?
   a. rennet   b. cheese   c. *P. shermanii*   d. whey

6. Which of these is/are added to cheese to produce many different flavors?
   a. rennin   b. bacteria   c. enzymes   d. curds

7. The process that turns dough into bread is called
   a. pasteurization   b. fermentation   c. selective breeding   d. curdling

8. When yeast eats dough, _____ is produced.
   a. hydrogen gas   b. nitrogen gas   c. carbon dioxide gas   d. oxygen

9. Yeast is a microorganism that feeds on
   a. bacteria   b. rennin   c. mold   d. carbohydrates

10. In the term *antibiotic*, the prefix "anti" means
    a. helpful things   b. life   c. microorganism   d. against

11. The medicine called *penicillin* is obtained from which of these?
    a. mold   b. bacteria   c. sick people   d. yeast

12. In the experiment on the effect of penicillin on mice, how many mice died in the group that did **not** get any penicillin?
    a. none   b. some   c. half   d. all

13. You could use selective breeding to create very big cattle by mating which types of cows and bulls?
    a. brown   b. dairy   c. large   d. fatty

14. Which of the following is an example of a purely *physical* trait in a dog?
   a. speed   b. hunting ability   c. size   d. friendliness

15. According to some people, there are at least how many drawbacks to selective breeding?
   a. one   b. two   c. three   d. four

True or False

Read each statement and indicate whether it is true or false. If it is false, correct the underlined word(s) to make the statement true.

1. Biotechnology means using or changing <u>organisms</u> to help make people's lives better.

1. _____

2. In the word "biotechnology," the prefix *bio-* means <u>life or living things</u>.

2. _____

3. The word biotechnology has been around <u>for thousands of years</u>.

3. _____

4. Archaeologists are <u>completely sure</u> about how cheese was first developed.

4. _____

5. Ancient people used <u>plastic bags</u> to carry their milk.

5. _____

6. Cheese is formed from milk because of an <u>enzyme</u>.

6. _____

7. Bread was most likely discovered <u>by accident</u>.

7. _____

8. The process that makes bread dough rise is <u>selective breeding</u>.

8. _____

9. <u>Bacteria</u> are responsible for making bread rise.

9. _____

10. An antibiotic is a substance that <u>kills the bacteria</u> that make people sick.

10. _____

11. The medicine penicillin is made from a substance extracted <u>from yeast</u>.

11. _____

12. The first time penicillin was given to a person, the result was <u>successful</u>.

12. _____

13. Selective breeding is a process that is <u>very recent</u>.

13. _____

14. A type of <u>behavioral trait</u> is an animal's ability to pick up scents and follow them.

14. _____

15. Selective breeding takes <u>only a short amount of time</u>.

15. _____

Short Answer

Answer the following questions in one or two complete sentences. For items 1 to 4, describe why each one is an example of early biotechnology.

1. Cheese-making:
2. Bread-making:
3. Developing penicillin:
4. Selective breeding:
5. What do the following events have in common: the discovery of how to make cheese, the discovery of how to make bread, and the discovery of penicillin?
6. Explain the difference between *rennin* and *rennet*.
7. Contrast the two main differences in cheese-making today as compared to how it was first done thousands of years ago.
8. How do archaeologists think yeast first got into dough and caused it to rise and form bread?
9. Describe the process that causes the yeast to make dough rise.
10. Briefly describe the story of how Dr. Fleming realized that *Penicillium* might have antibiotic properties.
11. Describe how Dr. Florey and Dr. Chain tested penicillin on mice. What were their results?
12. In your own words, explain what *selective breeding* means.
13. Explain what a farmer would have to do to create a type of apple that was yellow, if he first started out with mostly red apples.

Going Further

1. American poet Maxine Kumin wrote a poem about Anton van Leeuwenhoek's contribution to and improvement of the microscope, which greatly affected our understanding of some microorganisms. Using the Internet or another resource, find and read Kumin's poem. Using her poem as inspiration, write a poem about one of the examples of biotechnology discussed in this chapter (cheese-making, bread-making, the discovery of penicillin, or the use of selective breeding).

2. Create a collage of images that represents all the types of biotechnology you have read about in this chapter. You may use images from magazines, newspapers, and/or the Internet. Make sure you have enough images to represent all four types of biotechnology discussed so far.

CHAPTER 2

Biotechnology in the Environment

Essential Question:
How can we use living things to help keep the environment clean?

Contents

Can Ethanol and E85 Reduce Our Use of Fossil Fuels?

The last time you were riding in a car and it needed gasoline, you probably did not think much about the driver pulling into the nearest gas station to fill the tank. Gasoline is the main fuel for the approximately 135 million cars that are on the road in the United States. However, it is also a major source of pollution, which hurts our environment. Gasoline is an example of a **fossil fuel**, made from the fossilized remains of plants and animals from millions of years ago. Other examples of fossil fuels are coal, oil, and natural gas. When burned, fossil fuels produce carbon dioxide, which can damage Earth's atmosphere. Some scientists think that the increase in carbon dioxide from human activities in the past 50 years is likely a major cause of the reported global warming.

In the past few decades, there has been greater interest in the search for an alternative to regular gasoline for our vehicles in an attempt to reduce the amount of pollution. One major area of interest is the use of energy sources that have the ability to renew themselves; that is, to never run out. These sources of energy are called **renewable resources**. Examples of renewable resources are plants, the wind, and solar energy. People are interested in new energy sources such as **biofuels**, which are made from plants, because, unlike fossil fuels, biofuels do not release pollutants when burned. Another reason is because fossil fuels are in limited supply, but plants are not. People can keep growing new plants.

One alternative to gasoline that is becoming increasingly popular is ethanol. **Ethanol** is a clear, colorless, non-toxic liquid fuel made from the sugars found in plants. In the United States, ethanol is made mostly from corn; however, in other countries (like Brazil, the country with the largest ethanol produc-

tion) sugar cane is the primary source of ethanol. Since most of the corn in the United States is grown in the Midwest, most of our country's ethanol is also produced in that region. (See Figure 2-1.) Ethanol is mainly made as a result of the fermentation process. **Fermentation** is the process by which yeast cells eat the sugars in plants, producing the liquid ethanol (and also the waste gas carbon

Figure 2-1. In the United States, corn is the primary source for ethanol.

dioxide). This fermentation process is the same process that is used to create bread, which you read about in Chapter 1. As you learned in the previous chapter, biotechnology is the process of using living things to improve our lives. In fermentation, the living thing that we use is the yeast fungus; it helps us by making a fuel that can be used as an alternative to gasoline. (See Figure 2-2.)

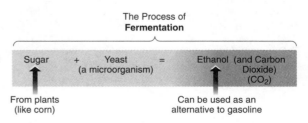

The Process of
Fermentation

Sugar + Yeast = Ethanol (and Carbon
(a microorganism) Dioxide)
(CO_2)

From plants   Can be used as an
(like corn)   alternative to gasoline

Figure 2-2. Fermentation of sugar by yeast produces ethanol (and carbon dioxide).

Ethanol was used as a fuel as far back as the 1800s. In the early 1900s, car-maker Henry Ford called ethanol the "fuel of the future," and he used a combination of ethanol and gasoline for his Model T car. (In fact, Henry Ford said, "There is fuel in every bit of vegetable matter that can be fermented.")

It was not until the late 1980s, however, that ethanol started to be used for the purpose of reducing pollution. The idea is that if automobiles burn less gasoline, they will produce less pollution. Unless specifically modified to do so, cars cannot run on pure ethanol. Instead, ethanol is blended with gasoline in varying amounts.

All gasoline-powered cars can run on a type of fuel called *E10*, which is made of 10 percent ethanol and 90 percent gasoline. Cars do not need to be modified or specially manufactured to use E10, which is sold in every state and makes up about one third of all fuel sales in the United States. Another alternative fuel that is growing in popularity in the United States is called **E85**; it is an ethanol–gasoline fuel mixture that consists of 85 percent ethanol and 15 percent gasoline. Unlike E10, the fuel E85 is not available everywhere. It is sold mostly in the Midwest; Minnesota has the greatest number of stations selling it. E85 is already a popular fuel choice in some other countries, such as Sweden and Brazil. (See Figure 2-3.)

Also unlike E10, E85 cannot be used to power all cars. The type of car that can use E85 is called a *Flexible Fuel Vehicle*. **Flexible Fuel Vehicles (FFVs)** can run on regular gasoline or on a combination of ethanol and gasoline, up to 85 percent ethanol. Flexible Fuel Vehicles are special versions of car models, so only some car models are FFV versions (there are stickers on the gas tank cap to let consumers know if they have an FFV). Most Flexible Fuel Vehicles in the United States are made by General Motors; however, Ford and Chrysler also make some FFV models. Aside from E85 fuel not being widely available yet, another drawback is that it reduces the fuel mileage—the distance the car can travel on a gallon of fuel—as compared to the same model of the car that is not an FFV. Flexible Fuel Vehicles typically get from 20 to 30 percent fewer miles for each gallon of fuel. For example, if one model of a car comes in a regular (gasoline) version and a Flexible Fuel version, and the regular car gets 25 miles per gallon, the FFV will get only about 18 miles per gallon. So even if E85 is priced lower than gasoline, it might cost more to use the combination fuel because you would have to fill the tank more often. Fuel mileage should be taken into consideration when comparing the cost to fill a tank using regular gasoline versus using E85. (See Figure 2-4.)

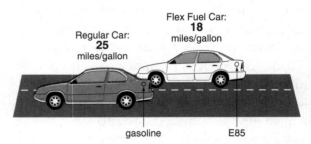

Figure 2-4. Flex Fuel Vehicles can run on E85 fuel, but they get fewer miles per gallon than the regular car that uses gasoline.

Despite these problems, the process of using yeast to make ethanol as an alternative to gasoline is growing in popularity. In the future, scientists hope to see this use of biotechnology lead to a decrease in the pollution caused by vehicles. Only time will tell if ethanol really is the "fuel of the future."

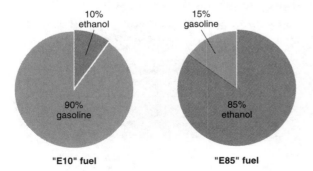

Figure 2-3. E10 fuel makes up about one third of all fuel sales in the U.S.; E85 is not as widely sold, but it is gaining in popularity.

Vocabulary Check

For each of the following terms, give a complete definition.

1. Fossil fuel

2. Renewable resources

3. Biofuels

4. Ethanol

5. Fermentation

6. E85

7. Flexible Fuel Vehicles

Multiple Choice

For each question, choose the letter of the answer choice that best completes the sentence or answers the question.

1. Approximately how many cars are there in the United States?
   a. 13 million   b. 35 million   c. 135 million   d. 153 million

2. Gasoline is an example of a(n)
   a. biofuel   b. renewable resource   c. ethanol   d. fossil fuel

3. Which of the following is ***not*** an example of a renewable resource?
   a. gasoline   b. plants   c. wind energy   d. solar energy

4. Which of the following is responsible for turning the sugar in plants into ethanol?
   a. bacteria   b. mold   c. yeast   d. wind energy

5. E85 is mostly sold in which part of the United States?
   a. Midwest   b. Southwest   c. Northeast   d. South

6. Flexible Fuel Vehicles get which percent lower gas mileage than regular vehicles?
   a. 0 to 20   b. 20 to 30   c. 30 to 40   d. 40 to 50

True or False

Read each statement and indicate whether it is true or false. If it is false, correct the underlined word(s) to make the statement true.

1. When burned, fossil fuels produce <u>oxygen gas</u>, which in large amounts can damage Earth's atmosphere.

2. There is <u>a limited supply</u> of plants to use as an energy source.

3. In the United States, <u>sugar cane</u> is the primary source of ethanol.

4. The country with the largest amount of ethanol production <u>is Brazil</u>.

5. Ethanol is made by a process called <u>fermentation</u>.

6. Ethanol was first used as a fuel for vehicles in the <u>early 1900s</u>.

7. E85 fuel has <u>less ethanol</u> in it than E10 fuel has.

8. <u>All types of cars</u> can run on E85 fuel.

9. Regular cars can travel more miles on one gallon of <u>gasoline</u> than FFVs can travel on one gallon of E85.

1. _____

2. _____

3. _____

4. _____

5. _____

6. _____

7. _____

8. _____

9. _____

Short Answer

Answer the following questions in one or two complete sentences.

1. Predict what will happen if we continue to burn fossil fuels as a fuel source.
2. Give two reasons that explain why people are interested in using renewable resources rather than fossil fuels as an energy source.
3. Fill in the blanks of this diagram to explain how ethanol is made.

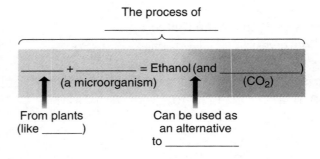

The process of
_____

_____ + _____ = Ethanol (and _____)
       (a microorganism)   (CO_2)

From plants   Can be used as
(like _____)   an alternative
              to _____

4. Explain why making ethanol is an example of biotechnology.
5. Compare E85 with E10 (give *two to three* ways in which they are different).
6. Evaluate the difficulties about using E85 to fuel a car (give *two* reasons).

Going Further

1. Make a **brochure** to persuade people that using ethanol will help the environment. Use the template on the following page to help you create your brochure. Include the following information in your brochure:

   - Cover page:
     - Title
     - Saying/phrase about why using ethanol is good for the environment
     - Picture/illustration

   - Inside:
     - Explanation about what ethanol is/how it is made
     - A pie chart showing what percent of E10 or E85 is made up of gasoline and what percent is made up of ethanol
     - Explanation about why using ethanol is good for the environment
     - What cars can use E85 (the name for the type of car, and some examples of car models). Use the following Web site to help you find which cars can use E85:
       http://www.e85fuel.com/e85101/flexfuelvehicles.php
     - List of where E85 can be purchased
       - List a few states that sell the most E85
       - Use the following Web site to find some fuel stations nearest to you that sell E85: ***http://www.afdc.energy.gov/afdc/locator/stations/*** (check off "Ethanol/E85" and enter in your zip code to find the nearest stations)

2. Create a *four-paragraph* **essay** about ethanol and E85. Create an outline of what you would like to write before you begin your essay. You may create your own outline or you may use the following outline to help you get started. Your teacher will provide you with a grading rubric.

Title of Essay: Ethanol and E85

Paragraph I. Main Idea: ***What ethanol is***

   A. **Subtopic:**

      1. Subtopic/supporting detail
      2. Subtopic/supporting detail
      3. Subtopic/supporting detail

   B. **Subtopic:**

      1. Subtopic/supporting detail
      2. Subtopic/supporting detail
      3. Subtopic/supporting detail

Paragraph II. Main Idea: *What Flex Fuel Vehicles and E85 are*

   A. **Subtopic:**

      1. Subtopic/supporting detail
      2. Subtopic/supporting detail
      3. Subtopic/supporting detail

   B. **Subtopic:**

      1. Subtopic/supporting detail
      2. Subtopic/supporting detail
      3. Subtopic/supporting detail

Paragraph III. Main Idea: *Advantages and disadvantages of using E85*

   A. **Subtopic:**

      1. Subtopic/supporting detail
      2. Subtopic/supporting detail
      3. Subtopic/supporting detail

   B. **Subtopic:**

      1. Subtopic/supporting detail
      2. Subtopic/supporting detail
      3. Subtopic/supporting detail

Paragraph IV. Main Idea: *Whether or not I would like to own a car that could run on E85*

   A. **Subtopic:** Your opinion (either **yes** or **no**)

      1. Subtopic/supporting detail
      2. Subtopic/supporting detail
      3. Subtopic/supporting detail

   B. **Subtopic:**

      1. Subtopic/supporting detail
      2. Subtopic/supporting detail
      3. Subtopic/supporting detail

3. Math skills: Below is a chart of the number of miles that each of the cars can go on one gallon of either gasoline or E85. Determine what percent the gas mileage decreases in a car when it uses E85 instead of gasoline. Following the Order of Operations, use the formula below to determine each answer.

$$\left[\begin{array}{l}\text{Percent decrease} \\ \text{when using E85}\end{array}\right] = 1 - \left[\frac{\text{Miles traveled on one gallon of E85}}{\text{Miles traveled on one gallon of gasoline}}\right] \times 100$$

Type of vehicle	Miles traveled on one gallon of gasoline	Miles traveled on one gallon of E85	Percent decrease when using E85
1) 2010 Ford Fusion FWD – FFV	18	13	
2) 2010 Toyota Sequoia 4WD – FFV	13	9	
3) 2010 Toyota Tundra 4WD – FFV	13	10	
4) 2010 Nissan Armada 2WD – FFV	12	9	

4. In 1925, Henry Ford had called ethanol the "fuel of the future"; however, ethanol has been around as a transportation fuel since the 1800s. Either on your own or with a partner use the information on the following Web site to create a *timeline* of important events in the history of ethanol as a transportation fuel. For longer pieces of information, you may paraphrase what is being said. If you would like, draw illustrations for a few of the events. Include information from the following dates: 1826, 1860, 1906, 1908, 1930s, 1945, 1974, 1978, 1988, 2002, 2008.

http://www.eia.doe.gov/kids/history/timelines/ethanol.html

5. Prepare a fermentation or ethanol **acrostic**. *Directions:* Create an acrostic poem for either the word "Fermentation" or "Ethanol" using words that describe them. The following words are examples of terms you may use: enzymes, fuel, gas.

How Does Bioremediation Work?

As you learned in the previous lesson, biotechnology can be helpful in our attempts to keep the environment free of pollutants. Unfortunately, our need for biotechnology to help clean up an area sometimes comes after a tragedy. In the morning hours of April 20, 2010, an explosion happened at an oil-drilling rig (a large machine used to drill for oil) in the Gulf of Mexico. About 64 kilometers (40 miles) off the coast of Louisiana, the *Deepwater Horizon* oil rig exploded, killing 11 workers. The incident, now called the **Deepwater Horizon oil spill**, was the world's largest accidental ocean oil spill to date. It ultimately leaked nearly five million barrels of oil (almost 206 million gallons) from the well, which is more than one kilometer down, on the bottom of the sea. By early August 2010, the well had finally been capped and sealed.

How did the *Deepwater Horizon* oil spill affect marine life and the rest of the ecosystem in the Gulf of Mexico? We may not know the full extent of the damage that has been done to the marine environment for quite some time. What we do know is that hundreds of seabirds (such as pelicans), marine mammals (such as dolphins), and endangered sea turtles have been sickened and killed by the crude oil both underneath and on the surface of the Gulf's waters. This loss is in addition to the thousands of fish and millions of invertebrates that cannot escape from the effects of the oil. Those animals that can be saved are being treated at special facilities. (See Figure 2-5a.)

Many marine animals were killed in a similar large oil spill that occurred off the coast of Alaska about 20 years prior to the *Deepwater Horizon* accident. On March 24, 1989, the **Exxon Valdez oil spill** demonstrated how devastating an oil spill can be

Figure 2-5a. A large oil slick is evident on the surface of the sea in the Gulf of Mexico; the oil spill came from the *Deepwater Horizon* oil rig accident.

on an ecosystem. The *Exxon Valdez* ship leaked more than 260,000 barrels (about 11 million gallons) of oil into Alaskan waters after it ran into a reef off Prince William Sound. The oil resulted in the death of over 250,000 seabirds, 2800 sea otters, 300 harbor seals, 250 bald eagles, and more than 20 orcas. (See Figure 2-5b.)

Figure 2-5b. The map shows the area of Prince William Sound in Alaska that was affected by the *Exxon Valdez* oil spill.

Approximate amount of oil spilled		
Oil Spill	Barrels	Gallons
Exxon Valdez	261,900	11,000,000
Deepwater Horizon	4,900,000	205,800,000

Figure 2-6. Oil spills have caused the deaths of thousands of seabirds, which die from hypothermia when oil gets stuck on their feathers. Some birds, like this one, are lucky to get rescued and cleaned after a spill.

There are a few reasons why an oil spill is so deadly to these sea creatures. The oil gets stuck on seabirds' feathers and on sea otters' fur, ruining the animals' ability to keep their skin warm and dry. As a result, the animals die of hypothermia (a very low body temperature). Animals can also die when they consume the oil (for example, when they try to clean the oil off their bodies) or when they eat other animals that are contaminated with oil. (See Figure 2-6.)

It can take many years and thousands of workers to clean up an oil spill. There are many ways an oil spill can be cleaned up, and the time it takes depends on the severity of the oil contamination. Among the many methods of cleaning up after a spill is one that involves using helpful bacteria to break the oil down into water and carbon dioxide. This method is called *bioremediation* and it works best in areas where the oil is not too thick. As you learned, the prefix *bio* means "living things." The root word, *remediation*, refers to the process of fixing a problem. The two terms together form the word **bioremediation**, which means using living things such as bacteria to help fix an environmental problem such as an oil spill. Bioremediation can be used to clean up both soil and water.

Bioremediation works by taking advantage of a natural process. All living things need to get their energy from a natural source, and some bacteria get their energy from the chemicals in oil. When bioremediation works, it happens in the following way: First, the microorganisms (that is, bacteria) in the area of the oil contamination *ingest* or "eat" the oil. Second, the bacteria *digest* the oil and convert it into water (H_2O) and carbon dioxide (CO_2) gas. The third step involves the bacteria releasing these substances into the atmosphere. (See Figure 2-7.)

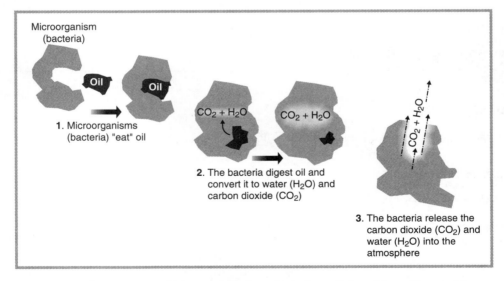

Microorganism (bacteria)

Oil

Oil

1. Microorganisms (bacteria) "eat" oil

$CO_2 + H_2O$

$CO_2 + H_2O$

2. The bacteria digest oil and convert it to water (H_2O) and carbon dioxide (CO_2)

$CO_2 + H_2O$

3. The bacteria release the carbon dioxide (CO_2) and water (H_2O) into the atmosphere

Figure 2-7. These steps of bioremediation show how living things (bacteria) can get rid of toxic oil from spills by converting it to water and carbon dioxide.

Fortunately for the people cleaning up the *Deepwater Horizon* oil spill, the Gulf of Mexico had two factors that helped the bioremediation process: the water already had a lot of oil-eating bacteria and the warm temperature of the water was an ideal environment for these bacteria to grow in. (Oil-eating bacteria were also helpful in the clean-up of oil at Prince William Sound.) Scientists cleaning up an oil spill do *not* add bacteria to the oil spill site. Rather, they add fertilizers that provide the specific nutrients that the oil-eating bacteria need in order to increase in number. Just as we need certain substances to grow and thrive, these bacteria need the nutrients in the fertilizer. By adding fertilizer that is rich in nitrogen and phosphorus, the scientists can help the population of oil-eating bacteria increase. The more bacteria at the oil-spill site, the faster the oil clean-up can occur. How effective the bioremediation process is may depend on the following factors: the type and amount of harmful chemicals present; the size and depth of the polluted area; and the conditions of the polluted area.

Using bioremediation to clean up an oil spill has many advantages over manual methods. First, it is a relatively safe method for cleaning up oil because it uses bacteria that are already in the area and no toxic chemicals need to be added. Second, it is relatively easy to carry out because the polluted soil or water can be treated at the site without having to transport the contaminated materials to another location. Third, it is not a costly method for cleaning up oil, compared to other methods, because very little equipment or labor is needed.

As you can see, this use of biotechnology has played an important role in helping to clean up the environmental mess left by the *Deepwater Horizon* oil spill as well as that left by the *Exxon Valdez* oil spill. With the help of oil-eating microorganisms, or *microbes*, Prince William Sound has been mostly cleaned up (though thousands of gallons of oil still remain on its beaches); and the Gulf of Mexico is slowly recovering. However, as with the *Exxon Valdez* incident, the negative effects of an oil spill can often be seen in the ecosystem near the spill site for years afterward; and we may well be seeing the harmful effects of the *Deepwater Horizon* oil spill for many years to come.

Lesson 2.2 Review

Vocabulary Check

For each of the following terms, give a complete definition.

1. *Deepwater Horizon* oil spill

2. *Exxon Valdez* oil spill

3. Bioremediation

Multiple Choice

For each question, choose the letter of the answer choice that best completes the sentence or answers the question.

1. In what year did the *Deepwater Horizon* oil spill occur?
   a. 1980   b. 1990   c. 2000   d. 2010

2. About how many gallons of oil were leaked into the ocean from the *Deepwater Horizon* accident?
   a. 206 million   b. 4,900,000   c. 11 million   d. 125 million

3. About how many seabirds were killed as a result of the *Exxon Valdez* oil spill?
   a. 28   b. 250   c. 2800   d. 250,000

4. How many steps are involved in the bioremediation process?
   a. one   b. two   c. three   d. four

5. What is the microorganism responsible for cleanup in bioremediation?
   a. yeast   b. bacteria   c. mold   d. algae

6. To help the bioremediation process, what do scientists add to an oil-spill site?
   a. water   b. oil   c. fertilizer   d. bacteria

True or False

Read each statement and indicate whether it is true or false. If it is false, correct the underlined word(s) to make the statement true.

1. The <u>Exxon Valdez</u> oil spill was the largest accidental ocean oil spill to date.

1. _____

2. Bioremediation works best in areas where the oil is <u>not too thick</u>.

2. _____

3. When bacteria "eat" the oil from a spill, they produce water and <u>oxygen</u> gas.

3. _____

4. Scientists <u>add bacteria</u> at an oil spill site for bioremediation to work faster.

4. _____

5. The fertilizer that the scientists added to the oil spills was full of <u>nitrogen and phosphorus</u>.

5. _____

6. The <u>fewer</u> bacteria at an oil-spill site, the faster the oil clean-up can happen.

6. _____

7. There are <u>many advantages</u> to using bioremediation to clean up an oil spill.

7. _____

8. Bioremediation is a <u>very expensive</u> method of cleaning up oil spills.

8. _____

Short Answer

Answer the following questions in one or two complete sentences.

1. Why is an oil spill so deadly for animals? Give *two* reasons.
2. Explain the *two* parts of the word "bioremediation."
3. Describe the *three* steps of bioremediation.
4. What two facts make the Gulf of Mexico an ideal place for bioremediation to happen?
5. Evaluate if using bioremediation as a method for cleaning up oil spills is beneficial. Give *three* reasons to support your evaluation.
6. How much bigger in size (amount spilled) was the *Deepwater Horizon* oil spill than the *Exxon Valdez* oil spill?

Going Further

1. On June 3, 1979, an oil spill occurred in the Yucatán Peninsula off the coast of Mexico. Similar to the *Deepwater Horizon* spill, the *Ixtoc I* oil spill leaked approximately 3,400,000 barrels of oil in the ten months before the leak was capped. The volume (amount) of oil is often given in either gallons or barrels. (a) If one barrel holds 42 gallons of oil, how many gallons of oil were leaked in this spill? (b) How does the amount of oil spilled during the *Ixtoc I* oil spill compare to that of the *Deepwater Horizon* spill?

2. With a group of your peers, create a live production of a news story that explains what happened during the *Deepwater Horizon* oil spill on April 20, 2010. You can have students pose as news anchors, interviewers, and people being interviewed. You will want to explain what happened, how it might affect the local ecosystem, and how biotechnology is used to help the area recover. This production can either be recorded on a video recorder or acted out in front of the class. You will be graded on how well you work with your team as well as how accurate and complete your news story is.

Why Is Composting a Beneficial Process?

Egg shells, onion skins, banana peels, grass clippings, and crumpled paper. What do these things have in common? You might say that these are items that you would find in a garbage can, but they are more than just garbage. With the help of biotechnology, these items can be turned into a nutrient-rich soil that can be used to help plants grow. (See Figure 2-8.)

Figure 2-8. By means of composting, these left-over food items can be turned into a nutrient-rich soil to help plants grow.

Everything **organic** (that is, something living or that comes from a living thing) will eventually decompose. **Composting** is a process that speeds up the decomposition of organic matter by providing the ideal conditions. Living things decompose when microscopic organisms break down the organic matter into simpler forms of matter. Most of the decomposition, about 80 to 90 percent, in a compost pile is done by the bacteria. Other microorganisms, such as yeast and some fungi, also help. There are bacteria already living on most things; so when a piece of food or other organic matter is left alone long enough, the bacteria on it will make it start to decompose. Composting takes advantage of this naturally occurring process by giving the bacteria the things it needs to grow. The more bacteria there are, the faster the organic matter breaks down.

So how does the composting process work? Compost piles need four things to work well: nutrients, water, oxygen, and decomposing microorganisms, called *decomposers.* The nutrients come from the organic material that is put in the pile. The types of things that can be put into a compost pile fall into two main categories: "browns" and "greens." The **browns** are organic materials that are high in carbohydrates and provide the element *carbon*; they include such things as autumn leaves, straw, and paper products (napkins, paper towels, paper bags, coffee filters, newspaper, and so on). The **greens** are organic materials that are high in protein and provide the element *nitrogen*; they include such things as grass clippings and food scraps (egg shells, coffee grounds, tea bags, apple cores, and so on). A compost pile works best when the brown items and green items are placed in alternating layers. (See Figure 2-9.)

After the organic material is put in a pile, there is not much more that has to be done.

Things Needed for Composting

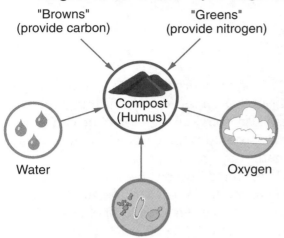

Figure 2-9. **Compost piles need four things to work well and produce humus: nutrients ("browns" and "greens"), water, oxygen, and decomposers.**

Figure 2-10. **A compost pile needs exposure to water and fresh air to work well.**

As mentioned before, a compost pile also needs water, oxygen, and decomposing microorganisms. Bacteria and other decomposers are already on the items that are put into the pile. Water and oxygen are necessary for the bacteria to grow well. The water is provided either naturally, from the rain, or when someone waters the pile if it has dried out. The compost pile gets oxygen by being turned every now and then, and also by being exposed to the air. If the compost pile is in a closed container, like an old trash can, holes have to be poked in the container for the air to come in. (See Figure 2-10.)

After the bacteria go to work, they start to break down the organic material. The time can vary, but it usually takes a few weeks to a few months for the material to decompose. The resulting product of the decomposition of organic material is called **humus** (pronounced hyoo-mus), or **compost**. Humus is a dark brown, nutrient-rich material; it can be used to enrich the soil where plants are grown to give them a boost of nutrients to help them grow well. (See Figure 2-11.)

Although there are many things that can be put into a compost pile, there are some things that cannot. Items that are *not* organic cannot be put into a compost pile because inorganic materials will not decompose. Remember, organic things are items that are living or came from living things. So anything that is not from an organism cannot be put into a compost pile. Metal, glass, and plastic are examples of things that are not organic, but they can be recycled. Other things that cannot be put into a compost pile—even though they are organic—include meat, bones, foods covered in oils, and dairy products. These items are not good for a compost pile because they can attract animals (who may try to eat the compost) and they can make the compost pile smell worse.

Composting is good for the environment because it takes things that might otherwise

Figure 2-11. **The product of a compost pile is a nutrient-rich material called humus.**

be thrown into the garbage (such as apple cores, egg shells, and paper towels) and turns those items into humus, which helps plants grow. It is an example of biotechnology because people are using decomposer microbes (bacteria, fungi, and yeast) to help make nutrient-rich soil for plants. Large compost piles such as those used by towns usually give off an odor, but people accept this because the benefits of composting are greater than the inconvenience of the smell.

Lesson 2.3 Review

Vocabulary Check

For each of the following terms, give a complete definition.

1. Organic

2. Composting

3. "Browns" for composting

4. "Greens" for composting

5. Humus / Compost

Multiple Choice

For each question, choose the letter of the answer choice that best completes the sentence or answers the question.

1. What percent of the decomposition of a compost pile is due to bacteria?
   a. 100 percent   b. 90 to 100 percent   c. 80 to 90 percent   d. 70 to 80 percent

2. Which of these are decomposing microbes that are involved in composting?
   a. fungi   b. yeast   c. bacteria   d. all of the above

3. Which of the following substances does a compost pile **not** need?
   a. metal   b. nutrients (nitrogen and carbon)   c. oxygen   d. water

4. Which of the following is considered a "brown" ingredient in a compost pile?
   a. paper bags   b. egg shells   c. tea bags   d. banana peels

5. Which of the following is considered a "green" ingredient in a compost pile?
   a. coffee filter   b. apple core   c. autumn leaves   d. straw

6. Which of the following items is the *only* one that can be put into compost?
   a. glass   b. plastics   c. inorganic items   d. organic items

True or False

Read each statement and indicate whether it is true or false. If it is false, correct the underlined word(s) to make the statement true.

1. "Green" ingredients provide the <u>carbon</u> in a compost pile.

    1. _____

2. A compost pile works best when the "brown" and "green" ingredients are placed in <u>alternating layers</u>.

    2. _____

3. Bacteria and other decomposing microorganisms are <u>added</u> to the compost pile.

    3. _____

4. The product of a compost pile is called <u>humus</u>.

    4. _____

5. Banana peels and crumpled paper are <u>just garbage</u>.

    5. _____

6. <u>Fungi</u> do most of the decomposition in a compost pile.

    6. _____

7. Organic things will <u>never</u> decompose.

    7. _____

8. A compost pile gets nutrients from the <u>organic material</u> that is put in the pile.

    8. _____

Short Answer

Answer the following questions in one or two complete sentences.

1. Explain how composting takes advantage of a natural process.
2. Imagine that organic things did *not* decompose. What would our Earth be like?
3. List at least *five* items that are considered either "brown" ingredients or "green" ingredients in a compost pile.
4. (a) Why does a compost pile need oxygen and water? (b) Explain how the compost pile gets the oxygen and water it needs.
5. (a) How long does it take a compost pile to turn into humus/compost? (b) What can be done with the humus once it is formed?
6. (a) Explain why things that are not organic cannot be put into a compost pile. (b) List at least *five* substances that cannot be put into a compost pile.
7. Explain why composting is an example of how biotechnology can help the environment.

Going Further

1. Draw a detailed diagram that shows what a compost pile should look like. Show the two different layers, drawing and labeling examples of items that would be in each layer. Also include in your picture the other substances that a compost pile needs to work. Remember to label these things as well.

2. Imagine you are the mayor of the town where you live. You care about the environment and would like to persuade the people of your town to start composting. Write a formal letter to the people of your town asking for their participation in a composting program. Your letter should do the following:

   - Explain what composting is and how it works
   - Explain the benefits of composting
   - Include a list of the things that can/cannot be composted
   - Describe how to make a compost pile

Since you really want the citizens of your town to take part in this project, think of some reward or incentive that you could offer people to encourage them to make a compost pile, such as free composting containers.

Your letter should be written in a proper letter format. Check with your teacher on how this should be done. Your letter will be graded according to the rubric provided by your teacher.

3. On a separate sheet of paper, use the correct terms to fill in the blank spaces in the diagram below to describe the substances a compost pile needs.

Things Needed for Composting

_____ (provide carbon)   _____ (provide nitrogen)

Compost
(_____)

_____   _____

_____

HOW CAN WE SIMULATE AN OIL SPILL?

Like the recent *Deepwater Horizon* oil spill off Louisiana, another human-made environmental disaster happened in 1989 off the coast of Prince William Sound in Alaska. The *Exxon Valdez* oil spill devastated the ecosystem around that area; the effects of the spill can still be seen today. Various methods were used to try to clean up the oil, such as using floating devices to try to contain the oil, chemical dispersants to help the oil evaporate, and high-powered machines to spray water onto the rocks and into the water.

Purpose

To evaluate the difficulty in cleaning up an oil spill by simulating a marine (ocean) ecosystem and what happens to that ecosystem when oil leaks into water. You will be working with a partner or in a team of three. Do NOT use live creatures.

Materials

1 pie pan
A handful of gravel
1 feather
250 mL water
100 mL colored water
Eye dropper
30 mL corn oil (vegetable oil)
20 cm nylon rope
A few drops of dish soap (provided by your teacher)

Note: Oil can stain your clothing; so if you get oil on your hands, wipe them on a piece of paper towel, not on your clothing.

Directions and Observations

Step 1. Take your gravel and gather it in one side of the pan. Pack the gravel as tightly as you can with your hand. With your partner, take turns practicing to gently rock the pan back and forth without letting the gravel move (this motion will simulate the tide once you put water in the pan). If the rocks move, gather them back to one side; pack them together; then try the motion again until the rocks do not move.

Step 2. Place the feather in the pan. This will simulate the feathers that are on the birds that live near the ocean. Do not touch this feather until your teacher tells you it is okay to do so.

Step 3. One of the team partners should pour the water into the pan. This water simulates the ocean that was surrounding the beach (the gravel).

Observation #1: Do you think this is high tide or low tide? Why?

Step 4. One of the partners should slowly pour the oil into the water in the pan, on the opposite side of the gravel, near where the water meets the edge of the pan. This simulates the oil slowly leaking from the ship into the ocean.

Observation #2: What does the oil spill look like?

One of the first things that scientists do in an oil spill is to try to contain the oil to stop it from spreading. They use a boom to do this, which is a series of floating tubes that form a long line. These are used to surround the oil, then a boat called a "skimmer" comes to suction up the oil. The nylon rope simulates the boom.

Step 5. One partner should take the nylon rope and try to surround the oil. The other partner will help to lift the pan up slightly above the table, then slowly rock the pan back and forth. *This simulates the tides coming in and out.* Try to make sure the water and oil stay within the pan.

Observation #3: Were the "booms" able to contain all of the oil?

Step 6. Remove the "boom" and set it aside.

Step 7. The teacher will come around and drop some dish soap into the water. This simulates the use of a chemical dispersant.

Observation #4: What happened when the soap went into the water and oil; was the soap able to remove the oil from the water?

Step 8. Each partner can take turns rocking the pan back and forth, as well as shaking it. This will simulate a storm that comes in (as happened a few days after the *Exxon Valdez* oil spill).

Observation #5: What happened to the rocks after the pan was shaken?

Observation #6: What does the feather look like now?

Step 9. Both partners can take turns trying to wash off the oil from the feather and the rocks by squirting them with the eye dropper. This simulates the high-powered hoses that sprayed the rocks and water. ***Note:*** Do **not** squirt the water on another person.

Step 10. Pick up the feather and some of the gravel (including the rocks near the bottom of the pan) and look at them.

Observation #7: Did the squirting get all of the oil off the feather and the rocks?

Conclusion and Evaluation

1. Were these good methods of cleaning up after an oil spill? Justify your answer.
2. Why is it important to try to clean up all of the oil after an oil spill?

Properly dispose of your mini-lab materials.

Graphing Skills

The Effect of Temperature on Bioremediation

When an oil spill occurs in the ocean, certain factors can influence the effectiveness of oil-eating bacteria in cleaning up the spill during bioremediation. These factors include such things as the water's pH level, amount of oxygen, amount of certain minerals (e.g., calcium, magnesium, and iron), as well as its temperature. Factors that increase the growth of oil-eating bacteria will increase the rate of bioremediation, since the more bacteria there are, the faster the oil will be cleaned up.

Below are the results of an experiment conducted by researchers who wanted to know how the water temperature would affect the rate of bioremediation. They took a 16-ounce sample of water where an oil spill had occurred and measured its temperature (20 °C) and the amount of oil-eating bacteria in the sample (about 18 million). The researchers then divided the sample into two 8-ounce beakers. In one beaker, they gradually heated the water over a flame. In the other beaker, they gradually cooled the water by placing it in a freezer. The researchers checked both water samples at every five-degree change to determine the amount of bacteria in each sample. The table at right contains the results of their experiment.

Draw a line graph that shows how the amount of bacteria changes depending on the temperature of the water they are in. After you have graphed the results, answer the questions below.

Effect of Temperature on Amount of Oil-Eating Bacteria in an Oil Spill	
Temperature of water (°C)	Amount of bacteria (in millions)
0	1
5	5
10	9
15	13
20	18
25	25
30	33
35	48
40	68
45	99
50	20
55	7
60	0
65	0

Questions

1. At what temperature will there be the greatest amount of bacteria? _____

2. At what temperature(s) will there be fewer than 5 million bacteria? _____

3. Calculate the change in the amount of bacteria for each 5°C increase in temperature:

0°C to 5°C = _____   5°C to 10°C = _____   10°C to 15°C = _____

15°C to 20°C = _____   20°C to 25°C = _____   25°C to 30°C = _____

30°C to 35°C = _____   35°C to 40°C = _____   40°C to 45°C = _____

45°C to 50°C = _____   50°C to 55°C = _____   55°C to 60°C = _____

60°C to 65°C = _____

4. What 5°C interval has the greatest *increase* in the amount of bacteria?
5. What 5°C interval has the greatest *decrease* in the amount of bacteria?
6. According to your graph, what would be the ideal 5°C temperature range for the process of bioremediation to happen at the fastest rate?
7. (a) What happens to the amount of bacteria after it reaches its peak?
   (b) Why do you think this happens?
8. (a) Analyze the graph to determine how the temperature of the water affects the amount of bacteria during the bioremediation of an oil spill.
   (b) What seems to happen to the amount of bacteria, going from 15°C to 45°C, at each 10-degree rise in temperature?
9. If you were a scientist working at the site of an oil spill, how might you use the information in this graph to help you in your bioremediation clean-up effort?

Going Further

1. As in most experiments conducted by scientists, the temperatures given in this example are given in degrees Celsius. To determine what the temperatures given in degrees Celsius (°C) would be in degrees Fahrenheit (°F), you would use the formula shown below. Use this formula to convert all °C temperature measurements given in this experiment into readings in degrees Fahrenheit.

$$°F = (9/5 \times °C) + 32$$

2. Research one or two other factors that can increase the number of oil-eating bacteria during bioremediation. Create a data table and graph that represents how those factors might affect the amount of bacteria available.

3. Research a few oil spills that have happened throughout the world as well as the average water temperature in the area where the spill occurred. For each oil spill, evaluate how well you think bioremediation would have worked in that area. Base your conclusion on the information you learned from your graph and the average water temperature of the area.

Student Activity: What Are the Steps of Bioremediation?

Bioremediation Activity

Directions

Cut out each diagram and place them in the correct order that they occur in
during the *three* steps of bioremediation. Next, paste them in the correct order
on a clean sheet of paper. Underneath each step, describe what is happening.
Also, include a definition of what bioremediation is at the top of your paper.
(See figures below.)

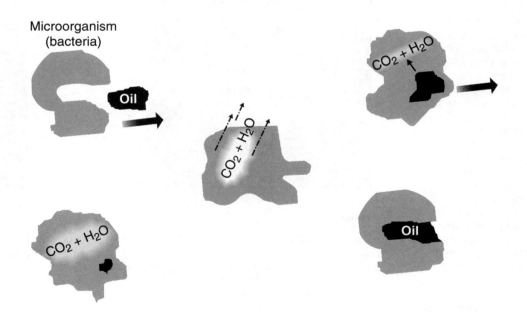

Chapter 2 Review

Vocabulary Crossword

Directions: *Each clue below is a definition of one of the vocabulary words that you learned in this chapter. On a printout of this page provided by your teacher, write the word that matches each definition inside the numbered vertical or horizontal spaces. All the vocabulary words from Chapter 2 are used in this puzzle.*

Across

2. When we use living things (like bacteria) to help fix a problem (specifically, an environmental problem such as an oil spill)
3. Plants that are used as an energy source
5. A process that speeds up the decomposition of organic things by providing ideal conditions
6. Something that is living or comes from a living thing
8. A fuel that is made from the fossilized remains of ancient plants and animals from millions of years ago
9. The process by which yeast feeds off the sugars in plants, producing the liquid ethanol (and also carbon dioxide)
10. Vehicles that can run on regular gasoline, or a combination of ethanol and gasoline, up to 85 percent ethanol (E85)
12. Organic materials that provide the nutrient called nitrogen, and include such items as fruit and vegetable scraps and grass clippings
13. When something fixes a problem
14. A clear, colorless, non-toxic liquid fuel that is made from the sugars found in plants

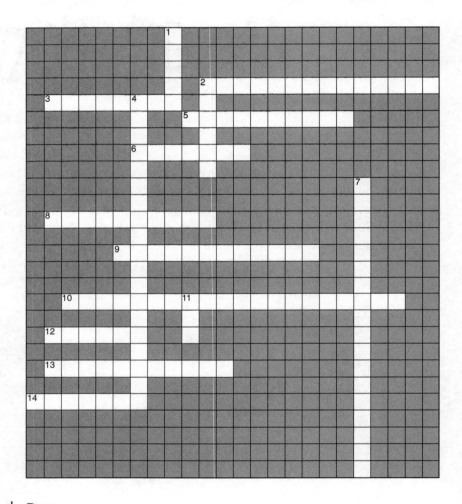

Down

1. The product of decomposition of organic material; a very dark, nutrient-rich soil
2. Organic materials that provide the nutrient called carbon, and include such items as leaves, straw, and paper products
4. Considered one of the most devastating man-made environmental disasters to happen from a ship
7. Energy sources that have the ability to renew themselves or which will never run out
11. An ethanol-gasoline fuel mixture that is consists of 85 percent ethanol and 15 percent gasoline

Multiple Choice

For each question, choose the letter of the answer choice that best completes the sentence or answers the question.

1. Which of the following is **not** an example of a fossil fuel?
   a. biofuel   b. gasoline   c. coal   d. natural gas

2. People are interested in using biofuels to try to reduce the amount of _____ caused by cars.
   a. noise   b. speed   c. traffic   d. pollution

3. What is the country with the largest ethanol production?
   a. United States   b. Brazil   c. Sweden   d. Germany

4. The useful product of fermentation is
   a. water   b. yeast   c. enzymes   d. ethanol

5. An alternative fuel made with only 15 percent gasoline is called
   a. E10   b. E15   c. E85   d. E100

6. The *Exxon Valdez* oil spill happened in which state?
   a. Alaska   b. Oregon   c. Washington   d. California

7. The animals that had the most deaths as a result of the *Exxon Valdez* oil spill were
   a. sea otters   b. seabirds   c. killer whales   d. harbor seals

8. Which living thing is responsible for "eating" the oil during bioremediation?
   a. mold   b. yeast   c. bacteria   d. fungi

9. The *Deepwater Horizon* oil spill affected marine life throughout the Gulf of
   a. Aden   b. Alaska   c. Mexico   d. Florida

10. An advantage of using bioremediation is that it is _____ than other methods.
    a. safer   b. easier   c. cheaper   d. all of the above

11. Which of these microorganisms does **most** of the decomposition in composting?
    a. bacteria   b. mold   c. fungi   d. yeast

12. The "brown" ingredients in a compost pile provide the nutrients with
    a. oxygen   b. nitrogen   c. carbon   d. phosphorus

13. Examples of "green" ingredients in a compost pile include
    a. grass clippings   b. paper bags   c. straw   d. dry leaves

14. The useful product of a compost pile is called
    a. paper products   b. food scraps   c. bacteria   d. humus

15. The product of a compost pile is mainly used to help the growth of
    a. birds   b. people   c. plants   d. mammals

True or False

Read each statement and indicate whether it is true or false. If it is false, correct the underlined word(s) to make the statement true.

1. Burning fossil fuels is <u>healthy</u> for the environment.

   1. _____

2. Ethanol is a <u>non-toxic</u> liquid.

   2. _____

3. The microorganism that makes ethanol from the sugars in plants is <u>bacteria</u>.

   3. _____

4. Ethanol is added to fuel to help the <u>environment</u>.

   4. _____

5. FFVs can run on <u>100 percent ethanol</u>.

   5. _____

6. The *Deepwater Horizon* well leaked a total of nearly <u>5 million barrels</u> of oil.

   6. _____

7. The *Deepwater Horizon* oil leak started when an <u>oil tanker</u> exploded at sea.

   7. _____

8. One problem with an oil spill is that the oil <u>sticks to the fur and feathers</u> of animals.

   8. _____

9. Bioremediation can be used to clean <u>water only</u>.

   9. _____

10. Aside from carbon dioxide, the other product of bioremediation is <u>water</u>.

    10. _____

11. Composting <u>slows down</u> the decomposition of organic things

    11. _____

12. There are <u>bacteria</u> on most living things.

    12. _____

13. The two categories of organic things that can be put in to a compost pile are <u>"browns" and "greens."</u>

    13. _____

14. A compost pile needs <u>water and oxygen</u> to help the bacteria do their job.

    14. _____

15. Composting usually takes <u>a few years</u> to work.

    15. _____

Short Answer

Answer the following questions in one or two complete sentences.

1. Explain why ethanol/E85 is a product of biotechnology.
2. How is bioremediation a type of biotechnology?
3. How is composting a form of biotechnology?
4. Give *two* reasons why people are looking for alternatives to fossil fuels to power vehicles.
5. Explain, in detail, how ethanol is made.
6. Contrast the fuels E10 and E85. (Give at least *two* differences.)
7. Contrast a Flexible Fuel Vehicle with a regular vehicle. (Give at least *two* differences.)
8. Explain why an oil spill at sea is harmful for animals that live in or near the ocean.
9. (a) Explain in detail how an oil spill can be cleaned up by using a type of biotechnology (describe all three steps). (b) What is the name of this process?
10. What do soil fertilizers have to do with bioremediation?
11. Describe the *five* things that a compost pile needs in order to work.
12. If a person wanted to make a compost pile, what steps would he/she need to take?
13. Explain why humus/compost is good for plants.

Going Further

1. On the next page is a template for a graphic organizer, which shows *three ways* that biotechnology can be used to help the environment. Copy this template onto a clean sheet of paper and, in each of the boxes, draw and label a picture showing items that describe the process and how it works.

2. Use the template on the next page to produce a one-page flyer titled "Ethanol: Saving the Earth One Corn Cob at a Time."

3. Imagine you are a news reporter for your local newspaper. Your editor wants you to write a newspaper story on the growing trend of using biotechnology to help the environment. Your newspaper article should explain the following:

   - Why people are concerned about the environment
   - What biotechnology is
   - How people are using biotechnology to help the environment (discuss the *three ways* we learned about in this chapter)

   This report should be written in the typical format for newspaper articles (see your teacher for how this should be done). You should include a headline, your name, the information, and at least one illustration with a caption. You might also want to include interviews (you can pretend that you interviewed people for your story). Your assignment will be graded according to the rubric given to you by your teacher.

How We Use Biotechnology
in the Environment

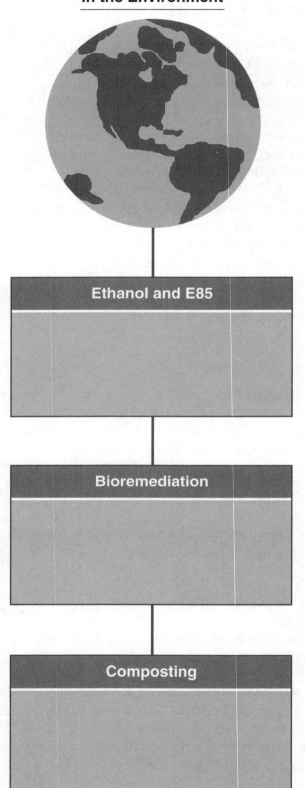

Ethanol and E85

Bioremediation

Composting

Ethanol: Saving the Earth One Corn Cob at a Time

Draw a picture that represents ethanol fuel here.
(Hint: corn, fuel, car)

Why is Ethanol good?
*Write the reasons why using ethanol in our cars is a good idea (give at least *three* reasons).

What is Ethanol?
*Write your explanation of what ethanol is and how it's made (include the name of the process that makes ethanol).

What cars can you use E85 in?
*Describe the type of car that can use E85.

*List some of the models of cars that can use E85.

What is E85?
*Draw a pie chart with a legend/key (include the *percent* composition for both gasoline and ethanol).

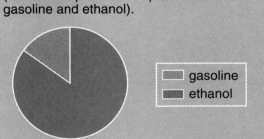

gasoline
ethanol

Where can you buy E85?
*List some states that sell the most E85.

*List the nearest places to where you live that sell E85.

DNA: Purpose, Structure, and Function

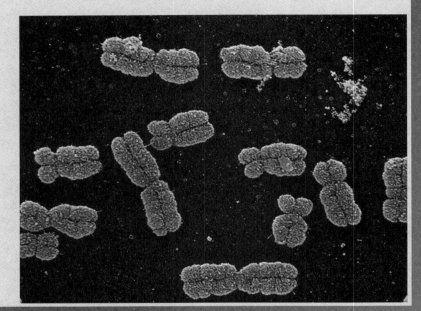

Essential Question:
How can understanding DNA help you better understand biotechnology?

Contents

So far, you have learned about many different ways that we *use* living things to help us. Now you will learn about how we can *change* living things to benefit us, which is also part of our definition of biotechnology. Specifically, we will be looking at how we can change the DNA of living things, and why we might want to do that.

What actually is DNA? The letters "**DNA**" stand for **d**eoxyribo**n**ucleic **a**cid. The DNA molecule contains the instructions for making an organism. DNA is often referred to as the "blueprint for living things," which compares it to the blueprint plans that an architect draws for building a structure. Similarly, DNA provides the plans for what a living thing will look and act like. Before we can learn more about what DNA is and how it works, we will look at how it was first discovered.

As far back as A.D. 1000, Hindu scholars noticed that certain diseases "ran in the family" and that children inherited parents' traits, or *characteristics*. However, most of our under-

standing of DNA came about within the past 150 years, starting with the work of Gregor Mendel (1822–1884). Mendel was an Austrian monk who is often called the "father of genetics" because his experiments (during the 1850s to 1860s) became the basis for our understanding of heredity today. **Genetics** is the study of how our traits are passed from one generation to the next. (See Figure 3-1.)

In his experiments, Mendel grew pea plants that had several contrasting traits, such as tall pea plants versus short pea plants, and yellow pea seeds versus green pea seeds. He studied these traits to see how they were passed from parent to offspring. What Mendel noticed was this: Traits are passed along in distinct patterns; and traits are controlled by two "factors" (what we now call *genes*). He realized that some factors were "dominant" over others and therefore showed up more often in the offspring. For example, yellow pea seeds are dominant over green pea seeds. Parents each passed one of their two factors (genes) to their offspring. The same parents' offspring can receive different sets of genes. Therefore, some offspring would get two copies of the dominant genes (yellow seeds) and show that trait; other offspring would get one copy of each gene, and still show just the dominant trait; and a few others would get two copies of the non-dominant, or *recessive*, genes (green seeds), and show that trait instead. Although not initially recognized for its greatness, Mendel's work was the foundation for future work in genetics. (See Figure 3-2 on page 66.)

After that point, scientists knew that genetic information was passed from parent to offspring, but they weren't sure how it worked. In 1928, a scientist named Frederick Griffith (1879–1941) conducted experiments on the

Figure 3-1. Gregor Mendel investigated the passing of characteristics from one generation to the next by studying the traits of the common pea plant.

Trait Studied	Alternate Forms	
Seed shape	◯ Round	Wrinkled
Seed color	Yellow	Green
Pod shape	Inflated	Wrinkled
Pod color	Green	Yellow
Flower color	Purple	White
Flower position	Along stem	At tip
Stem length	Tall	Dwarf

Figure 3-2. **The characteristics that Mendel studied occurred as easy-to-observe contrasting traits.**

bacteria that caused the illness pneumonia. From his experiments, he discovered that there was a molecule (which he called a *transforming principle*) that was responsible for passing along genetic information. This molecule remained a mystery until 1944, when researcher Oswald Avery (1877–1955) and his colleagues learned it was a molecule called *DNA* that was passing on genetic information. Before that, the accepted thinking was that *proteins* contained and passed along this information. Although Avery knew that DNA was the substance that passed information from one generation to the next, the structure and function of DNA still were not understood.

The structure of DNA started to be revealed in 1952, when a scientist named Rosalind Franklin (1920–1958) used a technique called *x-ray crystallography* to take a picture of DNA. She determined that the shape of DNA was formed by two strands

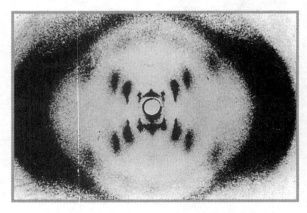

Figure 3-3. **The spiral shape of DNA was first revealed when scientist Rosalind Franklin used x-ray crystallography to take a picture of the DNA molecule.**

twisted in a spiral shape. Previously it had been thought that DNA was made of three strands. (See Figure 3-3.)

Franklin's now-famous x-ray photograph of DNA was then shown to two other scientists, James Watson and Francis Crick, without her knowledge. The photograph inspired Watson (1928–) and Crick (1916–2004), and helped them discover the shape and structure of DNA in 1953. (See Figure 3-4.) They determined that the shape of the DNA molecule was a double helix. A **helix** shape is a line

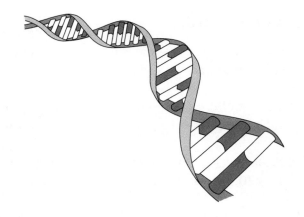

Figure 3-5. Watson and Crick also determined how the parts of a DNA molecule are paired up.

Figure 3-4. Scientists Watson and Crick determined that the shape of the DNA molecule was a double helix.

that is twisted around a central axis; and a **double helix** resembles two lines twisted around a central axis. Watson and Crick also

identified how the parts of the DNA molecule were paired (See Figure 3-5.)

For their discovery, Watson and Crick were awarded the Nobel Prize in Physiology or Medicine in 1962. Because the Nobel Prize is not awarded to someone who has already died, Rosalind Franklin was not honored as part of the discovery; she had died in 1958.

These scientists, along with many others, have contributed to our understanding of DNA. This discovery has formed the foundation on which much of our biotechnology knowledge is based.

Lesson 3.1 Review

Vocabulary Check

For each of the following terms, give a complete definition.

1. DNA

2. Genetics

3. Helix

4. Double helix

Multiple Choice

For each question, choose the letter of the answer choice that best completes the sentence or answers the question.

1. DNA is often referred to as the main _____ for living things.
   a. blueprint   b. chemical   c. substance   d. material

2. As far back as the year _____, Hindus noticed that certain diseases "ran in the family."
   a. 430 B.C.   b. A.D. 1000   c. 1865   d. 1951

3. Gregor Mendel is often called the "father" of which of these?
   a. biology   b. genetics   c. science   d. DNA

4. Mendel did scientific experiments using which of these organisms?
   a. people   b. fruit flies   c. mice   d. pea plants

5. Who discovered that DNA is the molecule that passes genetic information along?
   a. James Watson   b. Rosalind Franklin   c. Frederick Griffith   d. Oswald Avery

6. Watson and Crick determined that the shape of the DNA molecule is a
   a. circle   b. helix   c. double helix   d. rectangle

True or False

Read each statement and indicate whether it is true or false. If it is false, correct the underlined word(s) to make the statement true.

1. Most of our understanding of DNA has come about within the past 150 years.   1. _____

2. Mendel noticed that traits were passed down in distinct patterns.   2. _____

3. Mendel's experiments showed that traits did combine when passed down to the offspring.   3. _____

4. Griffith's experiment in 1928 showed that there was a molecule that was responsible for passing on genetic information.   4. _____

5. Watson and Crick took a picture of DNA using x-ray crystallography.   5. _____

6. The complete shape and structure of DNA was discovered In the year 1944.   6. _____

7. Rosalind Franklin was awarded the Nobel Prize for the discovery of the structure of DNA.   7. _____

Short Answer

Answer the following questions in one or two complete sentences.

1. Explain how Mendel conducted his famous pea plant experiments.
2. Summarize the ideas that Mendel learned from his pea plant experiments.
3. (a) What was discovered in Griffith's experiment in 1928? (b) What was discovered in Avery's experiment in 1944?
4. How did Rosalind Franklin contribute to our understanding of DNA?
5. What did James Watson and Francis Crick discover in 1953?

Going Further

1. Create a timeline of important events in the history of biotechnology that led up to the discovery of the structure of DNA. Use information from the following Web sites:

   http://www.accessexcellence.org/RC/AB/BC/6000BC-1700AD.php
   http://www.genome.gov/25019887#1900
   http://www.dnai.org/timeline/index.html

   Focus on the following years and people: 420 B.C. (Socrates); A.D. 1000 (Hindus); 1865 (Mendel); 1882 (Flemming); 1900 (DeVries, Correns, and Tschermak); 1902 (Sutton); 1909 (Johannsen); 1910 (Morgan); 1944 (Avery); 1950 (Chargaff); 1952 (Franklin); 1953 (Watson and Crick).

   For each of the events, summarize what happened in relation to our understanding of DNA and heredity. You may also want to draw an illustration for each event to help explain what happened in that year. Make sure that the events on your timeline are spaced appropriately (equal intervals between years).

   Why do you think most of the events happened within the past 150 years even though people have been speculating about heredity for thousands of years?

2. Evaluate if it was fair that Rosalind Franklin did *not* receive a Nobel Prize for her contribution to the discovery of the structure of DNA. Do you think that she should have received a portion of the Nobel Prize? Or do you think that her work was not as significant as that contributed by James Watson and Francis Crick? In one or two paragraphs, explain why you feel this was, or was not, a fair decision.

Lesson 3.2   What Is the Purpose of DNA?

Look around at your classmates. What do you notice about each other? You might notice that there is a wide variety of characteristics that your classmates have; some are male, some are female; some are tall, others are short; some have light skin, others have dark skin; some have naturally straight hair, others have curly hair. What accounts for these differences? The reason we all look different is because of the different *genes* that we have in our DNA. Yet even though we look so different, our DNA is basically the same. (See Figure 3-6.)

Figure 3-6. We all look different because of the different genes that we have; yet the structure of our DNA is basically the same.

Every organism has DNA, which is made up of a certain number of genes. All of an organism's DNA, which includes its genes, makes up what is called a **genome**. As mentioned in the first chapter, genes are the instructions that determine a certain characteristic in an organism. Our genes contain the instructions for everything from what gender we are, our height, eye color, if our hair will be curly or straight, if we might be more likely to get certain diseases, to how an organism behaves. In order for an organism to develop and function, it needs these instructions (genes) to specify its traits. Scientists currently estimate that our genome is made up of about 25,000 genes. Other organisms may have different numbers of genes. Humans share many of the same genes as other living things, especially those of the chimpanzee, which shares more than 98 percent of its DNA with humans. Yet, that small difference in our DNA has given humans many abilities that chimpanzees do not have, such as spoken language and other behaviors that involve higher brain functioning. (See Figure 3-7.)

When thinking about your own traits and genes, you may have noticed that you have

Figure 3-7. The chimpanzee shares more than 98 percent of its DNA with humans.

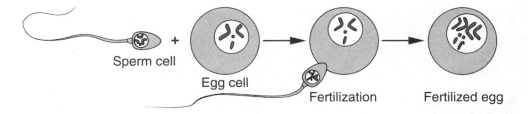

Sperm cell

Egg cell

Fertilization

Fertilized egg

Figure 3-8a. Fertilization occurs when the hereditary material of the egg cell combines with the hereditary material of the sperm cell.

some of the same traits as your mom and dad, which is no coincidence. Through the process of **heredity**, or the passing of traits from one generation to the next, you inherited half of your genes from your mom and half from your dad. When a living thing is produced by the joining up of heredity material from two parents (half from the mother and half from the father), the process is called **sexual reproduction**. Most organisms that can be seen without a microscope (for example, plants, animals, and people) receive their genes this way. The **reproductive cells** are the cells that pass on the genetic information to the offspring. In females, these are the *egg cells*; and in males, these are the *sperm cells*. The moment when the heredity material from the egg and sperm cells combine to create a new organism is called **fertilization**. (See Figures 3-8a and b.)

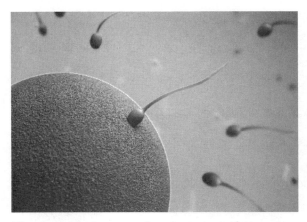

Figure 3-8b. A sperm has just started to enter the egg cell, which is many times larger than the sperm cells.

No two people share the exact same DNA, with the exception of identical twins. **Identical twins** develop when a fertilized egg splits in two, forming two separate organisms that have the same DNA and are always the same sex. Identical twins are different from *fraternal twins*, which develop when two eggs

Figure 3-9a. Identical twins develop when a fertilized egg splits in two, creating two separate organisms that have the same DNA.

are fertilized by two separate sperm cells at the same time. Fraternal twins, on average, have about the same number of genes in common as do any other pair of siblings born at different times; that is, about 50 percent. (See Figures 3-9a and b.)

By understanding how heredity works, we can understand a lot about the similarities

Figure 3-9b. Fraternal twins develop when two eggs are fertilized by two separate sperm cells at the same time; they have about the same number of genes in common as do any other pair of siblings, about 50 percent.

and differences between organisms. As already stated, all your genes came from both parents, with half coming from each parent. Why do siblings who come from the same parents look somewhat different? The answer is that each parent's reproductive cells have different genes that they pass on to their offspring. Each sibling will get some of the same genes from their parents, but also some different genes from them. This is why siblings often resemble each other, but do not look exactly the same unless they are identical twins.

There is a lot we can learn by studying DNA. Knowing that siblings share many of the same genes is very helpful for scientists who want to identify genes that cause diseases. If one sibling has a particular disease that the other does not, researchers may want to compare their DNA to determine if the disease was caused by a certain inheritable gene. Law enforcement personnel often use DNA to help them solve crimes. Since everyone (except identical twins) has his or her own unique DNA "fingerprint," people can be connected to crime scenes through body tissues (such as hair, saliva, and blood), which contain their DNA. These are just some of the many ways in which the use of DNA biotechnology can help people. (See Figure 3-10.)

Figure 3-10. Results from the analysis of DNA fingerprints can be used to argue guilt or innocence in criminal trials.

Lesson 3.2 Review

Vocabulary Check

For each of the following terms, give a complete definition.

1. Genome

2. Heredity

3. Sexual reproduction

4. Reproductive cells

5. Fertilization

6. Identical twins

Multiple Choice

For each question, choose the letter of the answer choice that best completes the sentence or answers the question.

1. Our genes are the instructions for our
   a. eye color   b. type of hair   c. height   d. all of the above

2. The genome of each person is made up of about _____ genes.
   a. 15,000   b. 25,000   c. 45,000   d. 65,000

3. The chimpanzee shares more than _____ percent of its DNA with humans.
   a. 65   b. 75   c. 85   d. 95

4. Children get how much of their genes from their mother?
   a. one quarter   b. one third   c. one half   d. three quarters

5. When two egg cells are each separately fertilized by two different sperm cells at the same time, what develops?
   a. identical twins   b. fraternal twins   c. more reproductive cells   d. one organism

6. Siblings share, on average, _____ percent of the same genes from their parents.
   a. 25   b. 50   c. 75   d. 100

True or False

Read each statement and indicate whether it is true or false. If it is false, correct the underlined word(s) to make the statement true.

1. Some organisms have DNA.   1. _____

2. DNA is made up of a certain number of genes, which are the instructions for certain traits.   2. _____

3. The living organism that the human is most closely related to is the baboon.   3. _____

4. Most organisms that can be seen without a microscope receive their genes through sexual reproduction.   4. _____

5. The reproductive cells made by females are called sperm cells.   5. _____

6. Identical twins always have <u>different</u> DNA.   6. _____

7. Studying DNA can help scientists learn about <u>diseases</u>.   7. _____

Short Answer

Answer the following questions in one or two complete sentences.

1. What can you conclude about your DNA and your classmates' DNA if you all have different traits?
2. Explain the purpose of our DNA.
3. Explain why children often look like both their mother and their father.
4. Compare and contrast identical twins and fraternal twins.
5. Explain why two siblings who were produced by the same two parents have some similar and some different traits.
6. Describe one way in which studying DNA can be helpful to people.

Going Further

When thinking about what a person's physical and behavioral characteristics are, scientists sometimes refer to the "nature *vs.* nurture" argument. Research this topic to learn more about both sides of the debate. Then your teacher will randomly assign you to one side in the debate to argue about which factor has a greater effect on people's characteristics. You will defend your position in a class debate, based on what you have researched.

Lesson 3.3 What Is the Structure of DNA?

You now understand that the purpose of DNA is to provide the instructions for what an organism will be. You may be wondering where the DNA is located and what it looks like. Understanding the structure of DNA is important to understanding how the instructions in the genes are "read."

To help picture DNA, imagine going inside a cell within an organism. DNA is located in every complete cell in an organism's body.

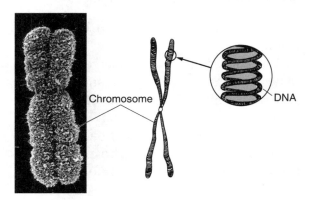

Figure 3-11. **The DNA is coiled up into structures called chromosomes at a particular time in the cell's life cycle; most of the time the DNA is unraveled in the nucleus.**

Specifically, it is located in the nucleus of the cell. The **nucleus** is the central part of a cell and is often referred to as the "brain" of the cell because that is where the instructions (DNA) for the cell's functioning are located. Inside the nucleus, you would see long strands of DNA (which could stretch to two meters in length) twisted and coiled up into structures called **chromosomes**. (See Figure 3-11.) (*Note:* The DNA is coiled up into the chromosomes at a particular time in the life cycle of a cell; most of the time it is unraveled within the nucleus.)

Two meters of DNA can fit inside a nucleus because the DNA is very small, and it is

twisted and folded so many times. If you were to unravel the chromosomes, you would see a long strand of DNA, divided into sections that contain the instructions for specific traits. These sections are the actual genes in the DNA. Yet, in the entire length of DNA, genes make up only about one to two percent of the whole DNA molecule. The function of the remaining DNA is largely unknown. Recent research has shown that this area, formerly called "junk DNA," does have a purpose, but it is yet to be fully understood.

Each species has a specific number of chromosomes, which always occur in pairs. Humans, for example, normally have 46 chromosomes in each body cell, or 23 *pairs* (two sets) of chromosomes. One set of 23 chromosomes comes from the mother; the other set of 23 comes from the father. Thus, in each pair of chromosomes, one is from the mother and one is from the father. The last pair of

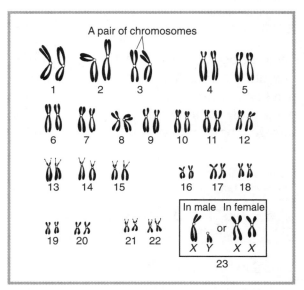

Figure 3-12. **Humans normally have 46 chromosomes in each body cell, or 23 pairs of chromosomes. One set of 23 is from the mother; the other set of 23 is from the father.**

---

chromosomes, called the *sex chromosomes*, determines whether a person will be male or female. If, at fertilization, a person gets one X and one Y chromosome, he will be male; if a person gets two X chromosomes, she will be female. (See Figure 3-12.)

As mentioned earlier in this chapter, Watson and Crick discovered that DNA was shaped like a double helix. While the scientific term *double helix* is used to describe DNA's shape, it can also be described as a "twisted ladder" or as a "spiral staircase." Watson and Crick also discovered the substances that make up this ladder. If we think of DNA as a twisted ladder, the steps or "rungs" of the ladder are made up of four substances, called **nitrogen bases**. The four nitrogen bases are *adenine, thymine, cytosine,* and *guanine*. Each nitrogen base will match up with only one other nitrogen base. Hence, adenine always pairs with thymine; and cytosine always pairs with guanine. These sets are called nitrogen **base pairs**, and they are held to-

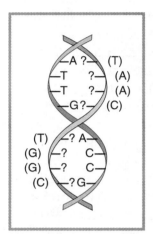

Figure 3-13. **The steps of the DNA "twisted ladder" are made up of four nitrogen bases that form base pairs: adenine always pairs with thymine; cytosine always pairs with guanine.**

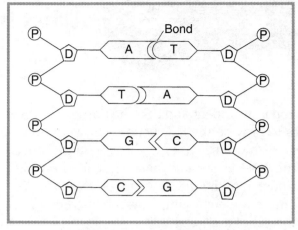

Figure 3-14. **Six substances—the four nitrogen bases along with the phosphate and five-carbon sugar molecules—form the nucleotide subunits that make up a DNA molecule.**

gether by chemical (hydrogen) bonds. (See Figure 3-13.)

The sides of the DNA "ladder" are made up of two substances: a *phosphate* and a five-carbon sugar called **deoxyribose**. The sides of the ladder are referred to as the "backbone" of DNA because, much like your backbone supports your body, the **sugar-phosphate backbone** provides the support for the DNA molecule. These six substances (each of the four nitrogen bases along with the phosphate and five-carbon sugar molecules) function together to form the **nucleotide subunits** that make up a DNA molecule. (See Figure 3-14.) In the next section, you will learn how DNA is not just a random sequence of nucleotide subunits; it is the molecule that codes for the proteins that make up an organism.

Lesson 3.3 Review

Vocabulary Check

For each of the following terms, give a complete definition.

1. Nucleus

2. Chromosomes

3. Nitrogen bases

4. Base pairs

5. Deoxyribose

6. Sugar-phosphate backbone

7. Nucleotide subunits

Multiple Choice

For each question, choose the letter of the answer choice that best completes the sentence or answers the question.

1. DNA is located in the _____ of a cell.
   a. nucleus   b. cytoplasm   c. membrane   d. outer layer

2. A molecule of DNA is about _____ meters in length.
   a. one   b. two   c. three   d. four

3. What percent of DNA is made up of functioning genes?
   a. 100   b. 80 to 90   c. 30 to 40   d. one to two

4. If a person is female, she would have which of the following sex chromosomes?
   a. XY   b. YY   c. XX   d. AA

5. Which of these terms is used to describe the shape of the DNA molecule?
   a. open book   b. turning fan   c. twisted ladder   d. flat-screen

6. There are ___ types of nitrogen bases that make up the "rungs" of the DNA molecule.
   a. two   b. three   c. four   d. five

True or False

Read each statement and indicate whether it is true or false. If it is false, correct the underlined word(s) to make the statement true.

1. DNA is in <u>only a few cells</u> of an organism.   1. _____

2. The nucleus is often called the <u>heart</u> of the cell.   2. _____

3. Sections of DNA that have instructions for a certain trait are called <u>genes</u>.   3._____

4. Humans have <u>23 pairs</u> of chromosomes.   4 _____

5. <u>Sex chromosomes</u> determine if a person is male or female.   5 _____

6. The nitrogen base adenine will always pair with <u>cytosine</u>.   6 _____

7. The backbone of a molecule of DNA is made up of <u>phosphate and deoxyribose sugar</u>.   7. _____

Short Answer

Answer the following questions in one or two complete sentences.

1. Explain how two meters of DNA can fit inside the nucleus of a cell.
2. Construct a sentence or two using all of the following words: chromosome, gene, DNA, cell, nucleus.
3. Speculate about why scientists used the term "junk DNA" to describe the parts of DNA that were *not* genes for specific traits.
4. On a separate sheet of paper, fill in the letters that represent the missing nitrogen bases on the following DNA diagram.

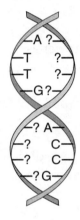

5. List the six substances that make up a DNA molecule's double helix.

Going Further

With a partner, construct a 3-D model of DNA using household items. Your model should be in the shape of a double helix and should have items that represent the four different nitrogen bases as well as the two substances that make up the backbone. Submit with your model an explanation of what each substance in your model is supposed to represent (for example, the bases thymine and guanine), and why you picked each material for your model. You will be graded according to the rubric provided by your teacher.

What Is the Function of DNA?

You have learned a lot about DNA so far, but you might still be wondering how DNA works. As mentioned previously, every cell of an organism with a nucleus has DNA in it. Not only is there DNA in all of these body cells, but it is the exact same DNA. This happens when each cell divides as an organism is growing. When the cells are dividing, the DNA is copied in a process called *DNA replication.* The process of **DNA replication** occurs when the DNA molecule unwinds and opens up like a zipper and then makes, or *replicates,* two identical strands to the original ones. (See Figure 3-15.)

Although there is the very same DNA in all body cells, only some parts of the DNA are "read" in each cell. For example, in the cells that are to become skin cells, only the DNA that has instructions for making skin cells is read, and those types of cells are produced. The DNA that codes for eye color, for example, is not read; so the proteins for that are not produced.

Every organism's body is made up of cells, and bodies are constructed of substances called *proteins* (among other substances). **Proteins** are large, chainlike molecules (of amino acids) that form the building blocks of cells, as well as making up the hormones and enzymes that keep our bodies functioning. Proteins make up everything about a person, such as their bones, muscles, blood, hair, and eye color. (See Figure 3-16.)

How do your cells read the DNA? Think of your entire set of DNA as the letters in an instruction book to build a model car. Only some parts of the writing are the actual instructions for building the car (just as only some parts of the DNA are genes that code for functioning proteins). Just as we would need to scan

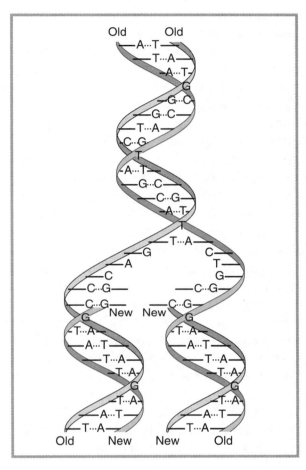

Figure 3-15. DNA replication occurs when the DNA molecule opens up like a zipper and then makes two new strands identical to the original ones.

Figure 3-16. Proteins are large, chainlike molecules (of amino acids) that form the building blocks of cells and keep our bodies functioning.

DNA: Purpose, Structure, and Function

the writing until we found the important part of the model car instructions, the cell scans the DNA, or *genetic code*, until it finds a particular gene, which then instructs the cell how to build the necessary protein.

There are about three million nitrogen base pairs that make up a person's DNA; and, as mentioned before, only about one to two percent of these base pairs are part of coding genes. The DNA of every organism is made up of the same four nitrogen bases, but what makes one organism's DNA unique from another's is the order in which they are arranged. In other words, every organism has its own specific "book of instructions" that is made up of a unique *linear sequence* of nitrogen base pairs (within the nucleotide subunits).

Just as we read letters in groups of words, the cell reads the DNA in groups of three bases called **codons**, or *triplet codes*. Some examples of codon triplets include: GAC, TTC, and AGT. The codons are grouped together in much the same way that the letters in our alphabet are grouped to form words. If part of a DNA molecule has the sequence TATCAAGATCCAGGGTCT, the cell reads the DNA in groups of 3-letter codons, like this: TAT CAA GAT CCA GGG TCT. (See Figure 3-17.) However, to actually make a protein, the DNA instructions must first be changed, or

transcribed, into RNA. The RNA molecule also has four nitrogen bases, but in RNA the base uracil substitutes for the DNA base thymine. Thus it is uracil that pairs with adenine in the RNA nucleotide sequences; and it is the RNA strand (delivering the instructions for the DNA molecule) that gets translated to build the proteins in the cell. (See Figures 3-18a and b.)

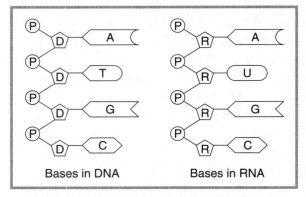

Figure 3-18a. RNA (like DNA) also has four nitrogen bases, but in RNA the nitrogen base uracil substitutes for the DNA base thymine.

When the cell reads the DNA, it knows to start building a protein when it comes across a *start codon*. The start codon is always TAC, and when the cell sees this in the DNA, it knows that it is the start of a gene. Similarly,

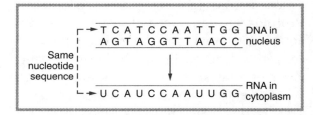

Figure 3-18b. In the RNA nucleotide (base) sequences, the base uracil pairs with the base adenine. It is the RNA strand (delivering instructions for the DNA molecule) that gets translated to build proteins in the cell.

there are also *stop codons* (ATT, ATC, and ACT), which signify that the gene is done and, as a result, the cell stops building the protein. The cell can then continue to read the DNA until it finds another start codon to build another

UUU	} Phe	UCU		UAU	} Tyr	UGU	} Cys
UUC		UCC	} Ser	UAC		UGC	
UUA	} Leu	UCA		UAA	*Stop*	UGA	*Stop*
UUG		UCG		UAG	*Stop*	UGG	Trp
CUU		CCU		CAU	} His	CGU	
CUC	} Leu	CCC	} Pro	CAC		CGC	} Arg
CUA		CCA		CAA	} Gln	CGA	
CUG		CCG		CAG		CGG	
AUU		ACU		AAU	} Asn	AGU	} Ser
AUC	} Ile	ACC	} Thr	AAC		AGC	
AUA		ACA		AAA	} Lys	AGA	} Arg
AUG	Met	ACG		AAG		AGG	
GUU		GCU		GAU	} Asp	GGU	
GUC	} Val	GCC	} Ala	GAC		GGC	} Gly
GUA		GCA		GAA	} Glu	GGA	
GUG		GCG		GAG		GGG	

Figure 3-17. The cell reads the DNA in groups of three bases called codons, or triplet codes.

protein. Using our comparison of a book, a start codon is like a capital letter at the start of a sentence; it is the signal for your brain to understand that you are about to read a new sentence. The stop codon is like punctuation at the end of a sentence, which is the signal for your brain that the sentence is complete.

Each codon calls for a specific amino acid. **Amino acids** are the substances that link together to build proteins. To make a protein, the amino acids form long, chainlike strands, which twist and fold in complex patterns. There are 20 different amino acids that make up the proteins in our body. Below is a list of the 20 amino acids that are used to build proteins.

Alanine	Glutamic Acid	Leucine	Serine
Arginine	Glutamine	Lysine	Threonine
Asparagine	Glycine	Methionine	Tryptophan
Aspartic Acid	Histidine	Phenylalanine	Tyrosine
Cysteine	Isoleucine	Proline	Valine

The diagram at right shows how the DNA in a gene is broken down into codons. Notice that each codon has a specific amino acid for which it codes. The amino acids are linked together to form a chain (that is, a protein). (See Figure 3-19.)

The number and sequence of the amino acids makes each protein unique; the specific

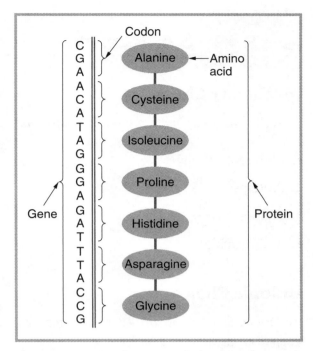

Figure 3-19. DNA in a gene is broken down into codons, and each codon has a specific amino acid for which it codes. The amino acids link together in a chain to form a protein.

way in which the protein twists and folds determines how it will function. For example, the protein made here could be one that determines a certain eye color. If the number and order of the amino acids were changed, it would form another protein with a different function.

Vocabulary Check

For each of the following terms, give a complete definition.

1. DNA replication

2. Proteins

3. Codons

4. Amino acids

Multiple Choice

For each question, choose the letter of the answer choice that best completes the sentence or answers the question.

1. During DNA replication, the movement of the DNA is compared to that of a
   a. zipper   b. spring   c. car   d. house

2. Proteins make up our
   a. blood   b. bone   c. muscles   d. all of the above

3. About how many nitrogen bases make up our DNA?
   a. 1 million   b. 2 million   c. 3 million   d. 4 million

4. Which one of these is ***not*** an example of a DNA codon?
   a. ACG   b. GGG   c. RPD   d. TTC

5. The codon that will always be at the start of a gene is
   a. TAC   b. TGA   c. ATC   d. GAT

6. There are _____ different amino acids that can be used to make up a protein.
   a. 3   b. 6   c. 12   d. 20

True or False

Read each statement and indicate whether it is true or false. If it is false, correct the underlined word(s) to make the statement true.

1. The DNA is <u>different</u> in every body cell of an organism.   1. _____

2. <u>Only some parts</u> of the DNA are "read" in each cell.   2. _____

3. Every organism has <u>a unique order</u> of nitrogen bases in their DNA.

3. _____

4. Codons are made up of <u>four</u> nitrogen bases in a row.

4. _____

5. Each codon represents a specific <u>protein</u>.

5. _____

6. The <u>size</u> of the amino acids makes each protein unique.

6. _____

Short Answer

Answer the following questions in one or two complete sentences.

1. Explain why a skin cell and a muscle cell would have the same DNA.
2. Compare and contrast a start codon with stop codons.
3. Explain how our DNA is similar to an instruction book.
4. List three amino acids that are used to help build proteins.
5. Fill in the blanks in the sentences below by using the following words:
   amino acids, codons, protein, genes.

   DNA is made up of thousands of _____, which are formed by a sequence

   of _____. These units code for specific _____, which make up a

   chain that forms a _____.

6. Fill in the four blank labels on the following diagram.

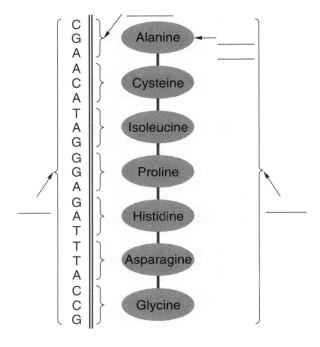

Going Further

1. An analogy is a comparison of two things that are otherwise not similar. For example, this section used the analogy of how an instruction book is similar to our DNA. Create your own analogy explaining what DNA is and how it works to turn information into proteins.

2. Math skills: (a) If there are three million nitrogen bases in human DNA, and about one to two percent of these nitrogen bases make up the coding genes, how many nitrogen bases actually make up genes? (*Hint:* Figure out what one percent and two percent would be). (b) Since there are three nitrogen bases in each codon, about how many codons do these three million nitrogen bases make up? (c) Approximately what percent of the codons represent the amino acid serine? (*Hint:* Round this result to the nearest whole number.)

How Can We Make a DNA MODEL?

Directions

1. Cut out the left side of the DNA molecule (on the sheet your teacher has handed to you).
2. Figure out which nitrogen base you need to pair up with each nitrogen base already on the DNA strand.

Note: To help you figure this out, complete these sentences:

Adenine always pairs with _____ .

Cytosine always pairs with _____ .

Thymine always pairs with _____ .

Guanine always pairs with _____ .

3. Cut out the nitrogen base that you need (from the free nitrogen bases) and paste it where it says "paste nitrogen base here." *Note*: There will be some left-over nitrogen bases that you may not use.
4. Cut out remaining backbone and paste it onto the nitrogen bases.
5. **Optional**–Color in your DNA model. You will need six different colors—one for each of the six substances that make up the DNA molecule.

Free Nitrogen Bases

T paste backbone here	**C** paste backbone here	**A** paste backbone here
T paste backbone here	**C** paste backbone here	**A** paste backbone here
T paste backbone here	**C** paste backbone here	**A** paste backbone here
T paste backbone here	**C** paste backbone here	**A** paste backbone here
T paste backbone here	**G** paste backbone here	**G** paste backbone here
G paste backbone here	**G** paste backbone here	**G** paste backbone here

Print This

Deoxyribose (sugar)	**T**	paste nitrogen base here
Phosphate		
Deoxyribose (sugar)	**G**	paste nitrogen base here
Phosphate		
Deoxyribose (sugar)	**A**	paste nitrogen base here
Phosphate		
Deoxyribose (sugar)	**C**	paste nitrogen base here
Phosphate		
Deoxyribose (sugar)	**C**	paste nitrogen base here
Phosphate		
Deoxyribose (sugar)	**A**	paste nitrogen base here
Phosphate		
Deoxyribose (sugar)	**G**	paste nitrogen base here
Phosphate		
Deoxyribose (sugar)	**T**	paste nitrogen base here
Phosphate		
Deoxyribose (sugar)	**A**	paste nitrogen base here
Phosphate		
Deoxyribose (sugar)	**C**	paste nitrogen base here
Phosphate		

Left Side of the DNA Molecule

Backbone

Deoxyribose (sugar)
Phosphate
Deoxyribose (sugar)
Phosphate
Deoxyribose (sugar)
Phosphate
Deoxyribose (sugar)
Phosphate
Deoxyribose (sugar)
Phosphate
Deoxyribose (sugar)
Phosphate
Deoxyribose (sugar)
Phosphate
Deoxyribose (sugar)
Phosphate
Deoxyribose (sugar)
Phosphate
Deoxyribose (sugar)
Phosphate

You've Got the key chain to My Heart

What better way to show someone you care about them than to give your heart to them. One way you can do this is to give them a key chain with the DNA instructions for a human (which, of course, includes the heart). You can make a key chain having the DNA sequence for other organisms as well (see chart below). This can be done this by making a key chain out of beads that matches a section of an organism's **genetic code** by using different beads to represent each nitrogen base.

Species	Section of their DNA code
Human (*Homo sapiens*) "heart"	GTTGCTGGTACAATGTGATAAAATGGGCTCCAGTGTT
Monarch butterfly (*Danaus plexippus*)	GAGGCTACCAAGTTTCCGATCTGTAGGAGATGCATT
Grizzly bear (*Ursus arctos*)	ATGACCAACATCCGAAAAACCCACCCATTAGCTAAA
Sunflower (*Helianthus annuus*)	TGAGATGTTAGAAGGTGCAAAATCAATAGGGGCCGG
Chimpanzee (*Pan troglodytes*)	TGACCCCGACACGCAAAATTAACCCACTAATAAAATT

Your key chain will contain two strands of beads. Each bead on one strand pairs up with its complementary bead on the other strand. Do you remember which nitrogen bases always pair up together?

Adenine ↔ _____

Guanine ↔ _____

> **Remember, the order of the nitrogen bases (A, T, C, and G) in the DNA is what makes each organism unique from other organisms.**

Materials

2 pipe cleaners (one white, one black), 1 key ring, an assortment of 4 different colored beads (in this case: red, blue, yellow, and white)

Directions

1. Choose one DNA code from the chart. (*Helpful hint:* Cross each letter off the list as you put the bead representing it on the chain.)

   Each nitrogen base will be represented by the following colors: adenine—red; thymine—yellow; cytosine—blue; and guanine—white.

2. Tie your two pieces of pipe cleaner (one black and one white) together a few times, and then wrap that around the side of the key chain ring.

3. Thread a bead onto the black pipe cleaner. Then thread the bead for the matching base onto the white pipe cleaner. For example, if you put a "C" on the black pipe cleaner, then you must put a "G" across from it on the white pipe cleaner.

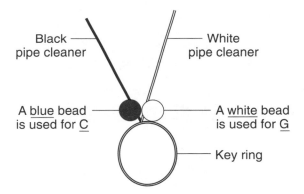

4. Continue putting the beads on the pipe cleaners, following the genetic code. For example, if the code is CATGA, you should have blue, red, yellow, white, and red beads on the black pipe cleaner; and you should have the matching bases on the white pipe cleaner.

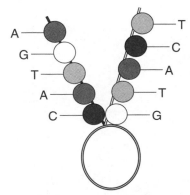

First DNA strand reads:	Opposite DNA strand should read:
C A T G A blue red yellow white red	G T A C T white yellow red blue yellow
(Colors of the beads)	(Colors of the beads)

5. Do not forget that the DNA molecule is twisted; once you have all the beads on the pipe cleaners, twist them twice to represent the double helix. If you want the beads to stay matched up in their correct pairs, you can use string every five beads to tie the two pieces of pipe cleaner together.

Wrap the pipe cleaner together at the end

Student Activity 1

How Do We Use a Codon Wheel to Identify Amino Acids?

De-Coding Amino Acid Codons

How do you know which combination of nitrogen bases will form the codon for a specific amino acid? By using this *codon wheel*, you can figure it out! (See below.)

The DNA Codon Wheel

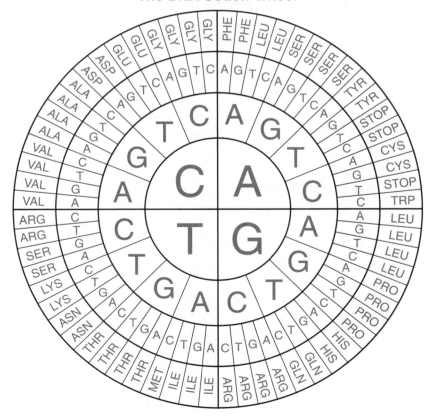

Amino Acids

ALA	Alanine	GLU	Glutamic acid	LEU	Leucine	SER	Serine
ARG	Arginine	GLN	Glutamine	LYS	Lysine	THR	Threonine
ASN	Asparagine	GLY	Glycine	MET	Methionine	TRP	Tryptophan
ASP	Aspartic acid	HIS	Histidine	PHE	Phenylalanine	TYR	Tyrosine
CYS	Cysteine	ILE	Isoleucine	PRO	Proline	VAL	Valine

For example, what amino acid does the codon CGT code for? Follow these steps to find out the answer. *Note*: The codon TAC is used only as a *start codon* to signal the start of a protein (much as a capital letter is used to signal the start of a sentence). There are three *stop codons*, which are used at the end of a chain of amino acids to signal that the chain is complete and the protein has been made.

Directions

1. Look at the *first letter* of the codon; in this case, it is C̲. Locate that letter on the inner circle of the codon wheel.
2. Look at the *second letter* of the codon; in this case, it is G̲. Locate that letter on the middle circle of the codon wheel within the area of that first letter. (That is, locate the G on the middle circle that directly connects to the C you located on the inner circle.)
3. Look at the *third letter* of the codon; in this case, it is T̲. Locate that letter on the outside circle within the section of the second letter (G).
4. Read (on amino acids chart) which amino acid that codon represents. Note that most amino acids are coded for by more than one codon triplet.

Practice Using the Codon Wheel

Part 1

Let us practice using the codon wheel. Here are some codons that are part of the DNA code. Find out which of the 20 amino acids each codon represents.

Codon	Amino acid
1. T G A	_____
2. G A A	_____
3. A A A	_____

4. T G T _____

5. G T G _____

6. A T C _____

7. C A G _____

Part 2

Can you determine which amino acids make up this section of a protein by looking at the following DNA base sequence?

C A T C C A A C C G C A T T T

Hint: Draw a line after each group of three letters to help you figure out the codons.

List the amino acids that are coded for in the base sequence above:

1. _____

2. _____

3. _____

4. _____

5. _____

Part 3

Use your codon wheel to determine which amino acid is coded for by each codon triplet. Write your answers on a printout of this crossword puzzle provided by your teacher.

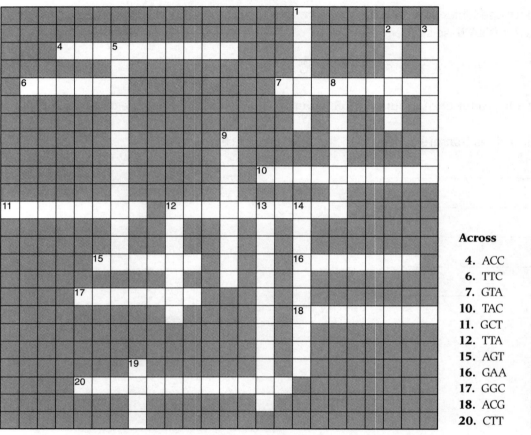

CODON CROSSWORD

Across

4. ACC
6. TTC
7. GTA
10. TAC
11. GCT
12. TTA
15. AGT
16. GAA
17. GGC
18. ACG
20. CTT

Down

1. CCC
2. CAT
3. TGT
5. AAA
8. ATA
9. GTT
12. CGA
13. CTA
14. TAT
19. ATC

Student Activity 2

What Is the Amino Acid Sequence of Insulin?

Insulin is a special type of protein called a *hormone*, and its job is to remove excess sugar from your blood after you eat. In this activity you will find out which amino acids make up this vital protein.

Directions

1. Divide the DNA sequence into codon triplets (remember, a codon is a group of *three* nitrogen bases in the DNA).

2. Determine which amino acid each triplet codes for by using your codon wheel.

Entire DNA sequence for insulin (made up of 53 codon triplets):

T A C C C C T A G C A A C T T G T T A C A A C G C G G A G T C A A
A C A T C A T A T A T A G T C G A A C T C T T A A T G A C G T T G
A A A C A T T T G G T T G T A A A C A C A C C C A G G G T G G A T
C A A C T C C G G A A T A T A A A C C A C A C A C C A C T T T C T
C C G A A A A A G A T A T G G G G C T T T C G T A T C

Codon	Amino Acid	Codon	Amino Acid	Codon	Amino Acid	Codon	Amino Acid
1. TAC	Methionine (start)	**15.**		**29.**		**43.**	
2. CCC	Glycine	**16.**		**30.**		**44.**	
3.		**17.**		**31.**		**45.**	
4.		**18.**		**32.**		**46.**	
5.		**19.**		**33.**		**47.**	
6.		**20.**		**34.**		**48.**	
7.		**21.**		**35.**		**49.**	
8.		**22.**		**36.**		**50.**	
9.		**23.**		**37.**		**51.**	
10.		**24.**		**38.**		**52.**	
11.		**25.**		**39.**		**53.**	
12.		**26.**		**40.**			
13.		**27.**		**41.**			
14.		**28.**		**42.**			

Vocabulary Crossword

Directions: *Each clue below is a definition of one of the vocabulary words that you learned in this chapter. On a printout of the next page provided by your teacher, write the word that matches each definition inside the numbered vertical or horizontal spaces. All the vocabulary words from Chapter 3 are used in this puzzle.*

Across

2. The substances that make up the "steps" of a DNA molecule: adenine, thymine, guanine, and cytosine
5. When the hereditary material in the sperm and egg cells combine to create a new organism
7. All of our DNA, including our genes
12. The cells that pass on the genetic information to the offspring
15. A shape that resembles a line twisted around a central axis
17. Groups of three nitrogen bases in the DNA molecule

18. Structures in the nucleus made up of twisted and coiled-up DNA
20. Formed when a fertilized egg splits in two, creating two separate organisms with the same DNA

Down

1. The study of how our traits are passed from one generation to the next; also called heredity
3. Process by which an organism receives half of its genes from each parent
4. Made of deoxyribose and phosphate, it is the main structural support of the DNA molecule
6. Pairs of (nitrogen) nucleotides; that is, adenine with thymine and guanine with cytosine
8. When the DNA molecule unzips and makes two identical strands
9. The passing of traits from one generation to the next

10. A shape that resembles two lines twisted around a central axis
11. The central part of a cell, often referred to as the "brain" of the cell
13. Large chainlike molecules that are the building blocks of cells, enzymes, and hormones
14. The substances that link together to form proteins
16. A branch of mathematics that deals with how likely it is that an event will happen
19. The instructions for making an organism

Multiple Choice

For each question, choose the letter of the answer choice that best completes the sentence or answers the question.

1. DNA is often compared to a _____ that is drawn by an architect.
   a. ruler   b. pencil   c. computer   d. blueprint

2. The man who is sometimes called the "father of genetics" was
   a. Gregor Mendel   b. James Watson   c. Francis Crick   d. Oswald Avery

3. Watson and Crick were aided by using a(n) _____ from Rosalind Franklin.
   a. letter   b. phone call   c. x-ray photograph   d. drawing

4. The structure of the DNA molecule was discovered in
   a. the 1850s   b. 1928   c. 1953   d. 1962

5. Our inherited characteristics are determined by
   a. genes   b. cells   c. diseases   d. viruses

6. Which organism has the most DNA in common with humans?
   a. baboons   b. chimpanzees   c. lemurs   d. gorillas

7. How many of your genes did you receive from your father?
   a. one quarter   b. one third   c. one eighth   d. one half

8. The nucleus is often referred to as the _____ of the cell.
   a. heart   b. brain   c. stomach   d. skin

9. Humans have _____ pairs of chromosomes.
   a. 12   b. 23   c. 32   d. 46

10. There are _____ different nitrogen bases in DNA molecules.
    a. four   b. five   c. six   d. seven

11. The base thymine always pairs with
    a. cytosine   b. guanine   c. adenine   d. phosphate

12. Proteins are made from chains of
    a. enzymes   b. chromosomes   c. sugars   d. amino acids

13. When our cells scan our DNA it can be compared to a person looking at a
    a. book   b. picture   c. television   d. crowd of people

14. Each triplet codon makes up the instructions for one
    a. DNA   b. gene   c. amino acid   d. sugar

15. One organism's DNA is different from another's due to the specific _____ of its nitrogen bases.
    a. shape   b. color   c. sequence   d. size

True or False

Read each statement and indicate whether it is true or false. If it is false, correct the underlined word(s) to make the statement true.

1. People noticed that certain diseases "ran in the family" as far back as <u>2000 B.C.</u>

   1. _____

2. Mendel used <u>apple trees</u> to do his experiments in genetics

   2. _____

3. Watson and Crick discovered that DNA was a <u>helix</u> shape.

   3. _____

4. Rosalind Franklin <u>did not</u> receive a Nobel Prize for her contribution to the discovery of the shape of DNA.

   4. _____

5. Our genes control traits such as <u>hair and eye color</u>.

   5. _____

6. <u>Fraternal twins</u> have the exact same DNA.

   6. _____

7. Police can use DNA to <u>help them solve crimes</u>.

   7. _____

8. The DNA molecule is <u>2 meters</u> in length.

   8. _____

9. Having both the X and Y chromosomes means a baby will be a <u>female</u>.

   9. _____

10. The shape of DNA is sometimes described as a <u>twisted ladder</u>.

    10. _____

11. Humans have <u>46 pairs</u> of chromosomes.

    11. _____

12. <u>Only some</u> cells in a person have the same DNA.

    12. _____

13. <u>Hormones and enzymes</u> are types of proteins.

    13. _____

14. Only about <u>30 percent</u> of our DNA are coding genes.

    14. _____

15. The <u>sequence</u> of amino acids makes each protein unique.

    15. _____

Short Answer

Answer the following questions in one or two complete sentences.

1. Explain why DNA can be compared to a blueprint.
2. Describe *three* facts that Mendel learned from his experiments on pea plants.
3. State the achievement that made Watson and Crick so famous.
4. Explain why you and your classmates all look different from each other.
5. Explain why children often look like both their mother and their father.
6. (a) Identify who would look more similar: fraternal twins or identical twins.
   (b) Explain how you determined your answer.

7. Use the following words in one or two sentences to show how they are related to each other: *DNA*, *cell*, *genes*, *nucleus*, and *chromosomes*.

8. Complete the following diagram (of a section of DNA) by writing the correct nitrogen base that belongs in each space.

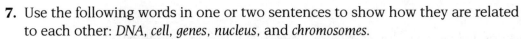

```
A    __
G    __
__    T
__    A
C    __
__    T
```

9. Draw a picture of a portion of a DNA molecule. Label the four different nitrogen bases as well as the substances that make up the backbone of the molecule.

10. If all body cells have the same DNA, explain why some cells become heart cells and other cells become liver cells.

11. Briefly explain how DNA goes from being a sequence of nitrogen bases to coding for the proteins that make up our bodies.

12. Use your codon wheel to determine which amino acids are coded for in this sequence: G A G G T C A A A T G A C G G T C A A G C A C C G T A A C A

1. _____	2. _____	3. _____	4. _____	5. _____
6. _____	7. _____	8. _____	9. _____	10. _____

Going Further

Much of what scientists have learned about our genes in recent years has come from the data obtained in the *Human Genome Project* (begun in 1990). With a partner, research the *Human Genome Project* and construct an informational poster (with some graphics) that explains what the project was. Be sure to include information on what the researchers discovered about the human genome. You will be graded according to the rubric provided by your teacher. Some Web sites are listed below to help you get started. You may want to use other Web sites to collect information as well. (Your teacher may discuss the ways in which you can know if a Web site's information is reliable.)

http://www.ornl.gov/sci/techresources/Human_Genome/home.shtml
http://www.genome.gov/
http://www.dnai.org/

CHAPTER 4

Mutations and Genetic Diseases

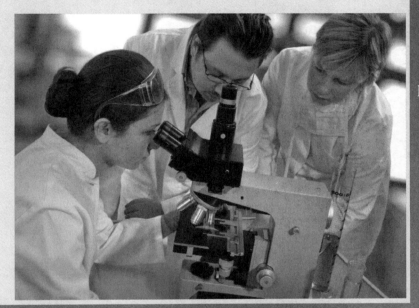

Essential Question:
How can mutations in DNA affect organisms?

Contents

What Causes Genetic Mutations?

When you hear the word *mutation*, you might think of characters you have seen in science fiction movies, such as a person with green skin or elastic limbs. However, this is not what scientists mean when they talk about mutations. A **mutation** is simply a mistake in the DNA that could result in a trait that is not normal. If you were to compare the DNA code to words in a book, a mutation would be similar to a typing error. Some mutations will not affect a person, particularly if they are part of the DNA that does not code for a gene. However, if the mutation is in a gene, it could have a wide range of effects. Mutations can result in a disease such as cancer, a disorder such as albinism (the lack of pigment), or a condition such as dwarfism (stunted growth). (See Figure 4-1.)

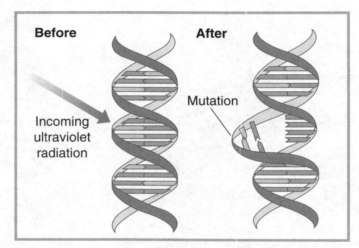

Figure 4-1. A mutation in a gene can have a wide range of effects on an organism and can even result in a disease such as cancer.

Let us see what a mutation could look like. Imagine that the series of triplet codes (of nitrogen bases) below is part of a normal DNA sequence:

A GG CTA TAC CTT TAT CGT AGG GGC ATA ATC GCA

Now suppose that the middle section is an entire gene. For the purposes of this exercise, we will pretend that this is a gene involved in making the human heart muscle.

Gene

A GG CTA **TAC CTT TAT CGT AGG GGC ATA ATC** GCA

If a mutation were to happen, it could be either inside or outside the gene. If the mutation occurred inside the gene, it could change the amino acid sequence and, as a result, the structure of the protein. If it were outside the gene, it might or might not affect the person (although most of our DNA does not code for any traits). Let us see what would happen if just one nitrogen base inside the gene were to be changed (from a G to an A).

A G G C T A **TAC CTT TAT CGT AGG GA̲C ATA ATC** G C A

If the sixth codon in this sequence had an adenine replace the guanine, it would change the amino acid that triplet coded. Since the shape of a protein is determined by the amino acids that are in it, the shape of the protein could change. This would lead to the protein not working properly. If this were a gene that was involved in making heart muscle, it could mean that the heart might not form properly.

How do these mutations happen? Before a cell can divide in two, its DNA undergoes replication to make two identical copies. Sometimes the cell will not perform this DNA replication perfectly, and a mistake suddenly occurs in the DNA sequence. These mistakes can happen while an organism is developing (for example, before a person is born) or as it develops and grows throughout its lifetime. The body does have mechanisms to catch and fix these mistakes. However, problems arise when the body does not get rid of or repair these mistakes. *Cancer* is an example of what happens when cells develop with a mistake in their DNA, yet they continue to replicate without getting fixed.

Once a genetic mistake occurs in a person, it could get passed on to offspring during reproduction. Mutations that are passed from one generation to a next are called **germ-line mutations** because the mistake is passed down through the *germ cells* (also called the *reproductive*, or *sex*, cells). People who are born already having germ-line mutations have inherited them. If a person has a germ-line mutation, the mistake occurs in each copy of his or her DNA, since the genetic sequence is identical in every body cell (also called *somatic* cells).

Some mutations occur during a person's lifetime; that is, they are not inherited. These are called **environmental mutations**. Factors that can lead to environmental mutations are called **mutagens** and include such things as tobacco, radiation (such as x-rays), sunlight (ultraviolet radiation), and certain chemicals or drugs. These environmental mutations sometimes lead to cancer; that is why people should take certain precautions, such as wearing sunblock or protective clothing and avoiding cigarettes and second-hand smoke. Note that even though people do not inherit environmental mutations, some people are born with genes that make them more likely than others to develop these mutations. (See Figures 4-2a and b.)

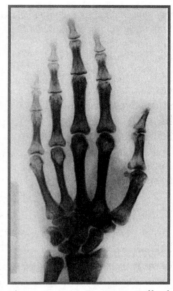

Figure 4-2a. **Factors, called mutagens, that can lead to environmental mutations include excessive sunlight and radiation (such as x-rays), chemicals, and tobacco.**

You might think all mutations are harmful to people; however, this is not true. Sometimes there can be a change in the DNA that produces a new trait that is either neutral (has no effect) or beneficial (has a positive effect. If a change in the DNA is positive, or at

Figure 4-2b. **Some environmental mutations can lead to cancer. People should wear sunblock to protect the DNA in their skin cells from damage by the sun's radiation.**

least not harmful, it eventually could become more frequent in a population and would no longer be considered a mutation. Slight changes that develop in the DNA and result in common differences in the traits of a species are known as **polymorphisms**. The word *polymorphisms* means "many shapes."

An example of polymorphisms is the slight changes in DNA that produce different eye colors in humans. New scientific research suggests that a mutation first arose about 6000–10,000 years ago that resulted in people having blue eyes. Prior to this, everyone had brown eyes. Because it was not a harmful mu-

tation, the trait eventually spread to more and more people. Now, in some parts of the world, between 20 and 40 percent of the population have blue eyes. All the common eye colors are polymorphisms because they result from the slight changes in DNA that are found among people. In addition, this trait is considered to be *polygenic* (meaning "many genes"), because at least eight genes are thought to determine a person's eye color.

Another example of DNA variations that are now common is the height range among human males and females. There is a certain range in height that is common for adults and is the result of slight differences in DNA. For example, in America, the range in height for adult females is mostly between 4′11″ and 5′8″; the range in height for adult males is mostly between 5′4″ and 6′2″. The slight differences in DNA that cause these variations provide another example of common polymorphisms. This trait is also considered to be polygenic, because more than one set of genes determines a person's height. (See Figure 4-3.)

Figure 4-3. **There is a certain range in height that is common for adults and is the result of slight differences in DNA. Most people's height falls in the middle range. This trait is considered polygenic, because more than one set of genes determines height.**

Vocabulary Check

For each of the following terms, give a complete definition.

1. Mutation

2. Germ-line mutations

3. Environmental mutations

4. Mutagens

5. Polymorphisms

Multiple Choice

For each question, choose the letter of the answer choice that best completes the sentence or answers the question.

1. Which of the following conditions results from a genetic mutation?
   a. green skin   b. albinism   c. elastic limbs   d. a head cold

2. Mutations can change the information in
   a. genes   b. amino acid sequences   c. proteins   d. all of these

3. If a person has a germ-line mutation, it is in _____ of their cells.
   a. none   b. some   c. most   d. all

4. Which one of these is *not* a typical mutagen that can change DNA?
   a. sunlight   b. oxygen   c. radiation   d. tobacco

5. Scientists think the polymorphism causing blue eyes appeared about
   _____ years ago.
   a. 6000–10,000   b. 3000–6000   c. 1000–2000   d. 500–1000

True or False

Read each statement and indicate whether it is true or false. If it is false, correct the underlined word(s) to make the statement true.

1. A particular mutation in a person's DNA can result in a condition known as <u>dwarfism</u>.

1. _____

2. A mutation can happen <u>only inside</u> a gene.

2. _____

3. A mutation would affect how the <u>protein</u> works.

3. _____

4. Our bodies <u>do not have</u> mechanisms for fixing mistakes in our DNA.   4. _____

5. <u>Germ-line mutations</u> are developed throughout a person's lifetime.   5. _____

6. <u>All mutations</u> are harmful to organisms.   6. _____

7. Having blue eyes started out as <u>a genetic mutation</u>.   7. _____

Short Answer

Answer the following questions in one or two complete sentences.

1. List examples of *three* conditions or diseases that are the result of mutations in DNA.
2. (a) Would a mutation outside a gene affect an organism? (b) Explain why or why not.
3. Explain how mutations can develop spontaneously in the DNA.
4. What is the main difference between germ-line mutations and environmental mutations?
5. Create a Venn diagram that compares and contrasts the definition of mutations and polymorphisms. Provide an example of each term.

Going Further

1. Create a poster to try to inform people about the dangers of smoking and of overexposure to ultraviolet rays (from sunlight). Include an explanation and a diagram of DNA that shows how these factors can cause mutations. You may use information from the following (or other reliable) Internet sources:

   About skin cancer: ***http://www.cancer.gov/cancertopics/wyntk/skin/page1***
   About lung cancer: ***http://www.cancer.gov/cancertopics/wyntk/lung***

2. Refer to the two amino acid (base) sequences below. Compare the normal strand of DNA to the mutated strand of DNA. Break the strand up into codons and then determine the amino acid sequence of each one in order to find which amino acid change occurred in the mutated strand of DNA. On a separate sheet of paper, write the two amino acid sequences; underline the one different amino acid.

   Original strand of DNA:

      T C C T T T A A A A C C G A A G T A C G A C T C T T C

   Mutated strand of DNA:

      T C C T T T A A A A C C G C A G T A C G A C T C T T C

What Types of Mutations Are There?

In the last section, you learned about mutations and what effects they can have on an organism. The type of mutation described occurs when one nitrogen base replaces another one. However, there are many different ways in which DNA can mutate. All gene mutations will most likely change the amino acid sequence; this will also affect how well the protein it makes will function. Below are five different types of gene mutations. By continuing our comparison of DNA to words in a book, we can see what each of the mutations looks like in a sentence.

A **point mutation** is one in which one nitrogen base has been replaced by another nitrogen base. In a sentence, if one letter were to replace another, it would cause the sentence to not make sense. Similarly, if you replace one base with another, it also changes the meaning of the DNA.

Original sentence: The big dog has one to**y**
Mutated sentence: The big dog has one to**g**

Below, a thymine is replaced by an adenine.

Original DNA sequence: A T A C T <u>T</u> A G T G A A
Amino acid sequence: Tyr   Glu   Ser   Leu

Mutated DNA sequence: A T A C T <u>**A**</u> A G T G A A
Amino acid sequence: Tyr   **His**   Ser   Leu

An **inversion** is a mutation in which a section of the DNA is reversed. This could happen to a small or a large section of the DNA.

Original sentence: The big d**og ha**s one toy
Mutated sentence: The big d**ah go**s one toy

In the DNA, the "TTAG" was reversed to be "GATT".

Original DNA sequence: A T A **C T T   A G**T G A A
Amino acid sequence: Tyr   Glu   Ser   Leu

Mutated DNA sequence: A T A **C G A   T T**T G A A
Amino acid sequence: Tyr   **Thr**   **Lys**   Leu

A **deletion** is a mutation in which one or more bases are removed from the DNA. Since the cell reads the bases in groups of three (that is, the codons), the bases shift over to fill in the gap in the sequence. Here is an example of how that would look if we use letters in a sentence (instead of bases):

Original sentence: Th**e** big dog has one toy
Mutated sentence: Thb igd ogh aso net oy

Below, a cytosine was deleted and as a result, the other nitrogen bases shifted over to fill in the gap.

Original DNA sequence: A T A **C**T T A G T G A A
Amino acid sequence: Tyr   Glu   Ser   Leu

Mutated DNA sequence: A T A T T A G T G A A
Amino acid sequence: Tyr   Asn   His
                                    Incomplete codon

An **insertion** is a mutation in which one or more bases are inserted into the DNA. Again, since the cell reads the DNA bases in groups of three, the bases shift over to make room for the new DNA.

Original sentence: The big dog has one toy
Mutated sentence: The big **nsg** dog has one toy

Below, the three bases "CGT" were added to the DNA sequence and, as a result, the other bases shifted over to make room.

Original DNA sequence: A T A C T T A G T G A A
Amino acid sequence: Tyr   Glu   Ser   Leu

Mutated DNA sequence:

ATA CTT AGT **CGT** GAA

Amino acid sequence: Tyr   Glu   Ser   Pro   Leu

The last two types of mutations described above, in which there is an insertion or a deletion (and the other bases have to move over to fill in the gap or to make room), are also both called **frame-shift mutations**. An arrow can be added to the sequences to show the direction in which the bases move.

Frame-shift mutation with a deletion:

Original sentence: The big dog has one toy

Mutated sentence: Thb igd ogh aso net oy

Original DNA sequence: ATA CTT AGT GAA

Mutated DNA sequence: ATA TTA GTG AA

Incomplete codon

Frame-shift mutation with an insertion:

Original sentence: The big dog has one toy

Mutated sentence: The big **nsg** dog has one toy

Original DNA sequence: ATA CTT AGT GAA

Mutated DNA sequence:

ATA CTT AGT **CGT** GAA

The way to determine which type of mutation has happened to a strand of DNA is to compare the original DNA strand with the mutated strand. Look at each nitrogen base in each sequence until you find the changes. Remember that if any bases have been inserted or deleted, the DNA in the sequence has probably shifted to make room for the new bases or to fill in the gap that was created.

Lesson 4.2 **Review**

Vocabulary Check

For each of the following terms, give a complete definition.

1. Point mutation

2. Inversion

3. Deletion

4. Insertion

5. Frame-shift mutation

Short Answer

Answer the following questions by comparing each sequence of DNA to identify which type of mutation(s) occurred. The same types of mutations may be used more than once. Note: Sometimes there may be two types of mutations present in one sequence. It also might be helpful to circle the DNA section that has been added, removed, or reversed and to draw arrows under the DNA that has shifted.

1.

DNA Base Sequences	Type of Mutation
a) Original DNA: T G T G A C C A G Mutated DNA: T G T C C A G	
b) Original DNA: T G T G A C C A G Mutated DNA: G A C C A G T G T	
c) Original DNA: T G T G A C C A G Mutated DNA: T G T A A C C A G	
d) Original DNA: T G T G A C C A G Mutated DNA: T G T G A C C T T A G	
e) Original DNA: T G T G A C C A G Mutated DNA: T A G T G C C A G	

2.

DNA Base Sequences	Type of Mutation
a) Original DNA: A A A C T A G G T C G T Mutated DNA: A A A G A T C G T C G T	
b) Original DNA: A A A C T A G G T C G T Mutated DNA: A A A C T A G G T A G T	
c) Original DNA: A A A C T A G G T C G T Mutated DNA: A A A C T A G C A C G T C G T	
d) Original DNA: A A A C T A G G T C G T Mutated DNA: A C T A G G T C G T	
e) Original DNA: A A A C T A G G T C G T Mutated DNA: A A A C T A G G C G T	

3.

DNA Base Sequences	Type of Mutation
a) Original DNA: T G A C C T C G G C A G Mutated DNA: T G A C G G C A G	
b) Original DNA: T G A A A T C G G C A G Mutated DNA: T G A C A T C G G C A G	
c) Original DNA: T G A A A T C G G C A G Mutated DNA: T G A A A T C G T A C C G C A G	
d) Original DNA: T G A A A T C G G C A G Mutated DNA: G A C G G C T A A A G T	
e) Original DNA: T G A A A T C G G C A G Mutated DNA: T G A A A G G C T C A G	

What Are Dominant and Recessive Alleles?

Now that you understand what a DNA mutation is and what it can do to an organism, you need to learn why not all mutations and traits are passed down from one generation to the next. Much of our initial understanding of heredity came from the work of Gregor Mendel. From his experiments, we learned that an organism will have certain **alleles** (variations of a gene), depending on which genes they inherit from their parents. For example, having brown eyes or blue eyes is the result of having certain alleles. Because of sexual reproduction, organisms inherit two alleles (at least) for every trait, one from each parent. The resulting trait that the organism shows depends on whether the alleles they received are dominant or recessive. A **dominant allele** will block expression of the other allele; the result is that the organism shows the dominant trait. An organism needs only one dominant allele (out of the two alleles) to show that trait. A **recessive allele**, on the other hand, is the one that can be blocked by a dominant allele. An organism needs two copies of the recessive allele to show that trait. (See Figure 4-4.)

We will use our example of brown eyes and blue eyes to see how this works. (You may recall that eye color is thought to be a polygenic trait; several sets of alleles contribute to the trait. However, for our purposes, we can concentrate on two main eye color alleles.) The "brown eyes" allele is dominant and the "blue eyes" allele is recessive. Alleles are usually represented by single letters, where the dominant allele is represented by a capital letter and the recessive allele is represented by the lowercase version of that letter. Since the "brown eye" allele is dominant, it is represented by the capital letter "B." The "blue eye" allele is recessive and is represented by a lowercase "b." Since the offspring would receive one allele from each parent, there are three possible **genotypes**, or combinations of alleles, that he or she could receive. The way that the genotype expresses itself as an observable

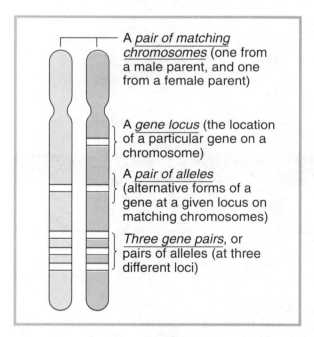

A *pair of matching chromosomes* (one from a male parent, and one from a female parent)

A *gene locus* (the location of a particular gene on a chromosome)

A *pair of alleles* (alternative forms of a gene at a given locus on matching chromosomes)

Three gene pairs, or pairs of alleles (at three different loci)

Figure 4-4. **The gene for one trait, such as eye color, exists at the same place on each member of a pair of matching chromosomes. Each gene has at least two alleles for the trait, one from each parent.**

Allele	Trait
B	Brown eyes
b	Blue eyes

Genotype	Phenotype
BB	Brown eyes
Bb	Brown eyes
bb	Blue eyes

trait in the offspring is called the **phenotype**. The chart shows the genotypes that a person could receive and the resulting phenotypes.

Some inherited diseases are controlled by a mutation in just one allele; one example is Tay-Sachs disease. This disease is caused by a small mutation in a person's DNA that affects a particular protein in the brain. The protein normally dissolves fat buildup in the brain; but because the protein does not form properly, it cannot do its job. The fat that builds up in the brain causes blindness, loss of muscle mass, seizures and, eventually, death. This usually affects children by the time they are three to five years old. The Tay-Sachs allele is recessive, so the only way that offspring can have the disease (that is, show the phenotype for it) is if they get two copies of the recessive allele (one from each parent).

Since the Tay-Sachs gene is a recessive mutation, the trait of being healthy and *not* having Tay-Sachs is dominant. This means that even if offspring have one dominant allele (no Tay-Sachs) and one recessive allele (Tay-Sachs), they will not have the disease. But it will still be possible for them to pass the recessive allele on to their offspring.

Allele	Trait
T	No Tay-Sachs disease
t	Tay-Sachs disease

Genotype	Phenotype
TT	No Tay-Sachs disease
Tt	No Tay-Sachs disease
tt	Tay-Sachs disease

An easy way to understand why not all traits or diseases are inherited is to use a Punnett square. A **Punnett square** is a chart that shows the possible combinations of alleles that could be created during fertilization. It is used to predict the probability of an organism having a certain disease or trait, since there is an equal probability of a parent contributing either allele to the offspring.

To use a Punnett square, draw a square with four boxes inside. Write the genotype of one parent above the square and of the other parent on the left, outside the square. Write the letter for each allele in its adjoining box. (See Figure 4-5.) The example given here

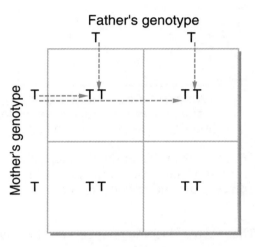

Figure 4-5. **This Punnett square shows the probability of a child being born with Tay-Sachs disease if neither parent has the Tay-Sachs (t) allele.**

shows what the probability would be of a child being born with Tay-Sachs disease if *neither* parent has the Tay-Sachs allele. Remember, the only way to get Tay-Sachs disease is if a person inherits two copies of the Tay-Sachs allele ("t"). The probability of having the disease would be 0/4, because the genotype "tt" is in none of the boxes. Another way of stating this is, there is a zero percent chance of this child having Tay-Sachs disease.

What happens if just one parent has the Tay-Sachs allele? When people have one allele for a disease but do not have the disease, they are called **carriers**; that is, they have one dominant and one recessive allele. In this example, the mother is a carrier but the father is not. By doing a Punnett square, we can learn a few things: (See Figure 4-6.)

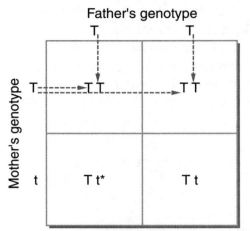

*Note: Whenever there is one dominant and one recessive allele, the capital letter is written first.

Figure 4-6. In this Punnett square, the mother (Tt) is a carrier for Tay-Sachs disease but the father (TT) is not.

- There is a 2/4 (50%) chance that the child will be a carrier ("Tt" genotype) and will not have Tay-Sachs. Although they will not have the disease, such children could still pass on the recessive allele for it to their own offspring.
- There is a 2/4 (50%) chance that the child will not have Tay-Sachs and will not be a carrier either ("TT" genotype).
- There is 0/4 (0%) chance that the child will have Tay-Sachs, because none of the boxes shows the "tt" genotype.

Lastly, what would happen if *both* parents were carriers of the Tay-Sachs allele? If we use a Punnett square, we can figure out the answer to this as well. (See Figure 4-7.)

- There is a 1/4 (25%) chance that the child will not have Tay-Sachs disease and will not be a carrier either ("TT" genotype).

- There is a 2/4 (50%) chance that the child will be a carrier but will not have Tay-Sachs disease ("Tt" genotype).
- There is a 1/4 (25%) chance that the child will inherit both copies of the recessive allele and thus will have Tay-Sachs disease ("tt" genotype).

An important thing to remember is that this Punnett square would apply each time the parents had a child. Let us use the last Punnett square as an example. If the parents in this situation had a child and that child was born with Tay-Sachs disease (the "tt" genotype, which has a 25 percent chance of happening), the next time they had a child, there would still be a 25 percent chance of the child being born with Tay-Sachs disease. Each birth is statistically an independent event and does not affect the others.

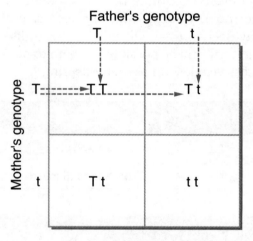

Figure 4-7. This Punnett square shows what could happen if both parents are carriers (Tt) of the Tay-Sachs allele.

Vocabulary Check

For each of the following terms, give a complete definition.

1. Alleles

2. Dominant allele

3. Recessive allele

4. Genotypes

5. Phenotype

6. Punnett square

7. Carriers

Multiple Choice

For each question, choose the letter of the answer choice that best completes the sentence or answers the question.

1. Much of our understanding of how different alleles can affect organisms came from the work of
   a. James Watson   b. Francis Crick   c. Gregor Mendel   d. Rosalind Franklin

2. Organisms inherit exactly _____ alleles for each gene.
   a. one   b. two   c. three   d. four

3. The trait for blue eyes is _____ allele.
   a. a dominant   c. both a dominant and a recessive
   b. a recessive   d. neither a dominant nor a recessive

4. If a person has the genotype Bb, he or she would probably have
   _____ -colored eyes.
   a. brown   b. blue   c. hazel   d. green

5. If a person has the Tt genotype for Tay-Sachs disease, he or she will
   a. have the disease and also be a carrier
   b. *not* have the disease but still be a carrier
   c. have the disease and *not* be a carrier
   d. *not* have the disease and *not* be a carrier

6. The probability that two carriers of the Tay-Sachs allele will have a child with Tay-Sachs disease is
   a. 100%   b. 50%   c. 25%   d. 0%

True or False

Read each statement and indicate whether it is true or false. If it is false, correct the underlined word(s) to make the statement true.

1. <u>All mutations</u> are passed down from one generation to the next.

1. _____

2. An organism needs only <u>one</u> dominant allele to show that trait.

2. _____

3. Expression of a <u>dominant</u> allele can be blocked by another allele.

3. _____

4. The combination of alleles that an organism has is called its <u>phenotype</u>.

4. _____

5. The only way a person can have Tay-Sachs disease is by getting <u>two</u> copies of the recessive allele.

5. _____

6. If two parents with genotype "Tt" had a child with Tay-Sachs disease, the probability of having another child with the disease is <u>25 percent</u>.

6. _____

7. A person who is a carrier of one recessive allele for a disease <u>can and will</u> develop the disease.

7. _____

Short Answer

Answer the following questions in one or two complete sentences.

1. Explain the difference between a dominant allele and a recessive allele.
2. (a) Two parents are going to have a child. The genotype of the mother is Bb and the genotype of the father is BB. What color eyes does each parent have?
(b) Using a Punnett square, explain the probability (in percent) of their child being born with blue eyes. (*Note*: You must draw the Punnett square and use words to explain the outcome.)
3. Describe what happens to a person when he or she has Tay-Sachs disease.
4. Explain why people would not know if they have the "TT" genotype or the "Tt" genotype for Tay-Sachs disease.
5. Draw a Punnett square to help you explain the probability of two parents who are both carriers of the Tay-Sachs allele having a child who does *not* have Tay-Sachs disease.

Going Further

1. A woman who has brown eyes has a child with a man who has blue eyes. Draw the two different Punnett squares that could describe this situation. For each scenario, state the probability (fraction or percent) of them having a child with brown eyes.

<table>
<tr><td>Scenario #1</td><td>Scenario #2</td></tr>
</table>

Scenario #1	Scenario #2
Probability of having a child with brown eyes: _____	Probability of having a child with brown eyes: _____

2. The following is a list of dominant and recessive traits. Create a survey of the members of your family to determine which have the dominant or the recessive traits. Communicate your results in the form of a bar graph. The recessive traits should be shown in one color and dominant traits in another.

Dominant traits	Recessive traits
Brown eyes	Blue eyes
Freckles	No freckles
Right handedness	Left handedness
Can roll tongue	Cannot roll tongue

What Types of Genetic Diseases Exist?

You now know how mutations can be passed down from parent to offspring, but you might wonder how diseases can result from a mutation in DNA. We first need to clarify the difference between a disease that you can catch from someone and a genetic disease. Unlike a *contagious disease*, which you can catch, a genetic disease cannot be spread through contact with an infected person or organism. A **genetic disease** is caused by a mutation in an organism's DNA, and it can be inherited. Contagious diseases are not inherited; however, some people may inherit a gene that makes them more susceptible to developing a particular disease.

There are two ways in which organisms can get a genetic disease: first, by inheriting the gene for that disease from one or both of their parents (depending on if the allele for the disease is dominant or recessive); second, by having the mutation occur in their DNA while they are developing. Some genetic diseases can have serious negative effects on a person and some even may be fatal. The term *genetic disorder* can also be used to describe a disease or condition that results from a mutation in DNA.

There are three main types of disorders caused by genetic mutations. The first type of disorder is caused by a mutation in one gene. As you already know, this could affect how or when a protein in the body is made. The mutation in the gene could be any of the types that you just learned about; that is, deletion, insertion, inversion, and so on. There are over 6000 known genetic diseases that are caused by a mutation in a single gene, including such conditions as Tay-Sachs disease, sickle-cell anemia, and Huntington's disease. Single-gene genetic diseases happen in about one out of every 200 births. (See Figure 4-8.)

The second type of genetic disease is caused by mutations in multiple genes; such conditions are more complex than diseases caused by just one gene. Examples of these include cancer, diabetes, high blood pressure, and Alzheimer's disease (a disorder that causes severe loss of short-term memory).

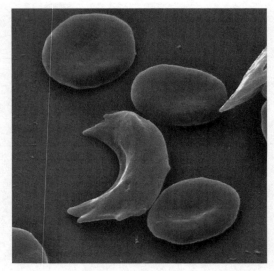

Figure 4-8. Many diseases, such as sickle-cell anemia (characterized by the abnormally shaped red blood cell shown here), are caused by a mutation in a single gene.

The third type of genetic disorder occurs when there is a mistake in the number or structure of chromosomes. Down syndrome, a disorder that results in short stature and mental retardation, is one of the most common examples of this type of disorder. This condition is caused by an extra chromosome 21. (See Figure 4-9.)

When a genetic disorder is caused by one gene, it can be caused by either a dominant or a recessive allele. When a genetic disorder is caused by recessive alleles it is called an **auto-somal recessive disorder**. (*Note*: The term

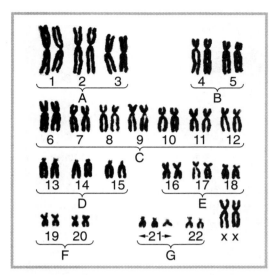

Figure 4-9. As shown in this photograph, some genetic disorders such as Down syndrome (which is caused by an extra chromosome 21) occur when there is a mistake in the number or structure of chromosomes.

autosome refers to the 22 matched sets of human chromosomes and does not include the set of XX or XY sex chromosomes). The only way to get this type of disorder is to inherit two copies of the recessive allele. This means that both parents would have to carry at least one recessive allele. If only one parent is a carrier and the other is not, there is no possibility that any offspring will have the disorder (review the section on Punnett squares to see why this is the case). (See Figure 4-10.)

Examples of autosomal recessive disorders include Tay-Sachs disease, cystic fibrosis, and sickle-cell anemia. The effects of Tay-Sachs were discussed in the last section. Cystic fibrosis is a genetic disease that mainly affects the respiratory and digestive systems. When a person gets this disease, it creates a problem in a protein that normally regulates the passage of salt through the cell membranes. Because there is a problem in the protein, the salt cannot pass through the cell membranes. This results in a build-up of salt inside the cells and a thick mucus layer outside the cells. This mostly happens in the lung cells, and leads to frequent respiratory

infections. There are treatments for the symptoms of this disease, but no complete cures at present.

Sickle-cell anemia is another genetic disease in which people have to inherit two recessive alleles in order to have the condition. This disease causes red blood cells to be shaped like a *sickle* (a type of blade); the misshapen cells get stuck in small blood vessels. Since red blood cells carry oxygen throughout the body and these cells are damaged, sickle-cell disease prevents proper blood flow, resulting in pain, anemia, and organ damage.

The other type of single-gene genetic disease is one that results from inheriting just one dominant allele. This is called an **autosomal dominant disorder**. If a person has one copy of the dominant allele, he or she will have the illness. This means that if one parent

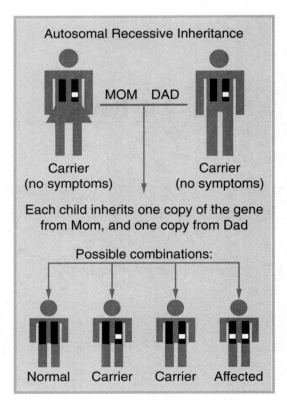

Figure 4-10. Autosomal recessive inheritance—in this case both parents are carriers. There is a 25 percent chance that their child will inherit both recessive alleles and have the disorder.

has the disorder, there is a 50 percent chance his or her offspring will have it. One example of this type of genetic disorder is Huntington's disease, a condition that leads to physical and mental deterioration during a person's adult life. (See Figure 4-11.)

Biotechnology companies are trying to help people with genetic diseases overcome their conditions and live healthier lives. In the next lesson, you will learn how.

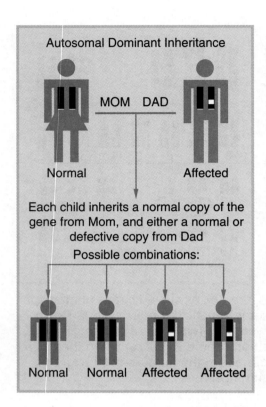

Figure 4-11. **Autosomal dominant inheritance—in this case only one parent has the disorder. There is a 50 percent chance that their child will have the disorder.**

Lesson 4.4 Review

Vocabulary Check

For each of the following terms, give a complete definition.

1. Genetic disease

2. Autosomal recessive disorder

3. Autosomal dominant disorder

Multiple Choice

For each question, choose the letter of the answer choice that best completes the sentence or answers the question.

1. There are _____ ways in which organisms can get a genetic disease.
   a. two   b. three   c. four   d. five

2. About how many known genetic diseases are caused by a mutation in one gene?
   a. 200   b. 600   c. 2000   d. 6000

3. Which of the following is an example of a disease caused by mutations in multiple genes?
   a. sickle-cell anemia   b. cystic fibrosis   c. Down syndrome   d. diabetes

4. An autosomal recessive disorder happens when someone inherits _____ recessive allele(s).
   a. zero   b. one   c. two   d. three

5. Misshapen blood cells are formed when a person has
   a. Alzheimer's disease   c. sickle cell anemia
   b. Tay-Sachs disease   d. cystic fibrosis

6. A person has a _____ chance of getting Huntington's disease if one parent has the condition.
   a. 100%   b. 75%   c. 50%   d. 25%

True or False

Read each statement and indicate whether it is true or false. If it is false, correct the underlined word(s) to make the statement true.

1. Another term for a genetic disease is a genetic <u>sequence</u>.   1. _____

2. Genetic diseases caused by a mutation in one gene happen in about one in every <u>500</u> births.   2. _____

3. Some genetic diseases are caused by a mutation in <u>multiple genes</u>.   3. _____

4. Down syndrome is caused by an <u>extra chromosome 21</u>.   4. _____

5. With a genetic disease caused by a recessive allele, there is no way offspring can get it if <u>only one</u> parent has the allele.   5. _____

6. <u>Tay-Sachs disease</u> causes thick mucus to form on the outside of lung cells.   6. _____

Short Answer

Answer the following questions in one or two complete sentences.

1. How is a contagious disease different from a genetic disease?
2. Explain the *two* ways in which someone can get a genetic disease.
3. What are the *three* main types of genetic disorders? Give *one* example of each type.
4. Explain the difference between an autosomal recessive disorder and an autosomal dominant disorder.
5. Describe the main symptom(s) of each of the following genetic disorders: Alzheimer's disease; cystic fibrosis; Down syndrome; Huntington's disease.

Going Further

Genetic Diseases Research Project

Purpose: To learn more about the effects of certain mutations in DNA, you will research a genetic disease or disorder and then present your findings to the class.

Part 1: Working with a partner, you will research one genetic disease, either randomly selected or assigned by your teacher. Collect your information and record it on a poster so you can present it to the class. Illustrate how this particular disease can be inherited, either by using a Punnett square or another diagram. You will be graded according to the rubric given by your teacher.

Presentation Checklist: Include the following information in your presentation:

- ❏ A general overview about what the disease/disorder is
- ❏ Who is more likely to get the disease; for example, is a certain gender or ethnic group more likely to have the disease than another group?
- ❏ A list of the symptoms/effects of the disease/disorder
- ❏ A diagram or Punnett square showing how the disorder is inherited
- ❏ Genetic cause—if it is caused by a single-gene mutation (dominant or recessive), mutations in multiple genes, or a mutation in a certain chromosome
- ❏ How the disease/disorder is tested for or diagnosed
- ❏ What the current treatment is, if any; and if there are treatments that scientists would like to use in the future, if applicable
- ❏ Any current research being done on the disease
- ❏ Any other interesting information about the disease

Part 2: The other part of your project is to write down some of the information given in other students' presentations. You will record this information on your own Genetic Diseases Information Chart. For each genetic disease/disorder, you will write down the main symptoms, the mutation that causes it, and who is most likely to inherit the disorder (if this is applicable).

How Do Biotechnology Companies Help Us?

Now you know that genetic diseases can have devastating effects on people. So, what can the field of biotechnology do to help people with these conditions? The answer lies in the work being done by biotechnology companies. **Biotechnology companies** are businesses in which scientists use their knowledge of DNA to research genetic diseases and try to develop medications to treat people who suffer from

Figure 4-12. **Scientists at biotechnology companies use their knowledge of DNA to research genetic diseases and to try to develop medications for people.**

them. There are biotechnology companies all over the world; many of the biggest ones are located right here in the United States. (See Figure 4-12.)

One of the ways biotechnology companies can help people is by conducting genetic testing. **Genetic testing** is the examination by scientists of people's DNA to find out if they are carriers of any genetic diseases or if they have a genetic disease. Some tests cannot determine for certain if a person will get a genetic disease, but they can find out if they are *more likely than others* to develop the disease. There are currently over 1200 different genetic tests that people can be given; only about a dozen are approved by the FDA (Food and Drug Administration), the government agency whose main job is to make sure that medicines are safe for people.

Newborn babies are routinely screened for genetic diseases. Adults may choose to get additional genetic testing, too. One reason for more testing is that, before they decide to

have their own children, some people may want to know if they could pass along any genes for diseases to their offspring. They may also want to know if they have the genes for a disease (such as Alzheimer's or Huntington's disease) that might show up later in life. This knowledge could have a big impact on their families, so they may want to be better prepared in case such an illness develops in the future. (See Figure 4-13.)

How do scientists know which genes are responsible for causing a specific genetic disease? In order to find the gene (or genes) responsible for causing a certain genetic disorder, researchers must gather DNA samples from many people, including one group of people who have the genetic disease and another group who do not. Then, the researchers carry out a process known as **DNA sequencing**, in which they de-

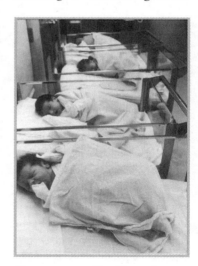

Figure 4-13. **Newborn babies are routinely screened for genetic diseases, a practice that can help save lives.**

termine the order of the DNA nitrogen bases in each of the samples. Next, they compare both groups' DNA sequences to identify the differences between them. The differences in their DNA may be the genes that cause the genetic disease. If the scientists can compare the DNA of people who are related (and in which some have the genetic disease and others do not), their chances of finding the genes for the disease will increase. This is because the DNA of related people will likely be quite similar, so any differences in the DNA would stand out more.

Once scientists know which genes cause a genetic disease, they can use their knowledge of a person's DNA to try to fix the mutation in their genes. One way is to develop a medicine that might work by doing the job that the missing or damaged protein cannot do. However, developing a medicine that treats people with a genetic disease can take a very long time. It is typical for a medicine to take about 20 years to be ready before it can be given to the public. Another option is called *gene therapy*, which will be discussed in the next chapter. There are currently no cures for genetic diseases, but there are some treatments that help people have fewer symptoms of the diseases. (See Figure 4-14.)

Genetic testing for the general public presents some *ethical*, or moral, concerns. One concern is that people might not want to know if they are likely to develop a genetic disease later in life, especially if there is nothing they can do to prevent it and it might not

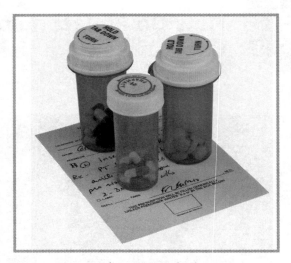

Figure 4-14. **By knowing which genes cause a particular disorder in a person, scientists can try to develop a medicine that does the job the missing or damaged protein cannot do. However, developing such a medicine can take a very long time.**

even happen. Others might argue that knowing early can prepare them to deal with the genetic disease if and when they get it. At present, genetic testing is not common. It is usually done only after interested individuals go for genetic counseling once they discuss it with their doctor.

Another concern people have about screening everyone's DNA is that it might lead to genetic discrimination. Discrimination occurs when people are treated unfairly because of some characteristic they have. In the case of **genetic discrimination**, people may be at a disadvantage due to the results of a genetic test. For example, if people undergo genetic testing and discover that they are likely to develop a genetic disease, employers might not want to hire them and health insurance companies might not want to insure them. In 2005, a basketball player on the Chicago Bulls team was traded to another team after he refused to be tested for a gene that might cause him to develop a heart problem. To prevent such genetic discrimination from happening, a law called *GINA*, or the *Genetic Information Nondiscrimination Act*, was signed on May 21, 2008. This law makes it illegal to treat someone unfairly based on the results of a genetic test. In other words, it makes it illegal for employers to require a person to take a genetic test in order to be hired or to keep a job. It also makes it illegal for health insurance companies to deny coverage to people based on the results of a genetic test.

Vocabulary Check

For each of the following terms, give a complete definition.

1. Biotechnology companies

2. Genetic testing

3. DNA sequencing

4. Genetic discrimination

Multiple Choice

For each question, choose the letter of the answer choice that best completes the sentence or answers the question.

1. Many of the biggest biotechnology companies are in which country?
   a. the United States   b. Canada   c. Switzerland   d. Iceland

2. The U.S. government agency that can approve a company giving genetic tests is the
   a. FBI   b. EPA   c. IRS   d. FDA

3. To find genes that cause disease, scientists need to use DNA from people who
   a. have the disease   c. are related
   b. do not have the disease   d. all of the above

4. Developing a medicine that gets approved for people with a genetic disease can take as long as
   a. 5 years   b. 10 years   c. 15 years   d. 20 years

5. The law passed to help protect against genetic discrimination is called
   a. AGIN   b. GAIN   c. GINA   d. INGA

True or False

Read each statement and indicate whether it is true or false. If it is false, correct the underlined word(s) to make the statement true.

1. Biotechnology companies research genetic diseases and <u>develop medicines</u> to help people with those diseases.

1. _____

2. Babies <u>are not screened</u> for genetic diseases.

2. _____

3. Some genetic diseases, such as <u>Down syndrome</u>, might not develop until later in life.

3. _____

4. Currently, there are <u>many cures</u> for genetic diseases.

4. _____

5. In 2008, a law was signed to try to prevent genetic <u>information</u>.

5. _____

Short Answer

Answer the following questions in one or two complete sentences.

1. What are *three* things that people can learn about themselves from genetic testing?

2. Describe *two* reasons why a person might want to undergo genetic testing.

3. Describe *three* steps that a scientist would take in order to find the genes that cause a specific genetic disease.

4. Once the gene that causes a specific disease has been found, how can biotechnology companies help people with that condition?

5. Identify the *two* important things that "GINA" made illegal.

Going Further

1. With a partner, write a list of reasons for (pro) genetic testing and a list of reasons against (con) genetic testing. For each point raised, explain why it would be either helpful or harmful.

2. Debate: Pick one of the following debate questions and write your response. Whichever side you choose, give *three* reasons to support your opinion.

   a. Would you participate in a study in which your DNA was linked to your health records and other personal information, but *only* if your identity was kept a secret? Explain why you feel this way.

   b. Would you participate in a study in which your DNA was linked to your health records and other personal information, but your identity was *not* kept a secret and the information could be given to various groups, such as your school or your future employer? Explain why you feel this way.

   c. Would you want to be tested to find out if you have a gene that *may* cause a particular type of cancer, even if you knew there was no current cure for it? Explain why or why not.

PUNNETT SQUARES AND PROBABILITIES

You can use your knowledge of Punnett squares to help predict the probability of specific genotypes (and the resulting phenotypes) of offspring. You can also make predictions about the genotypes and phenotypes of the parents if you only know the phenotypes of their offspring.

Part 1: Predicting the genotypes and phenotypes of the offspring

A woman who has freckles has a child with a man who has no freckles. Draw the two different Punnett squares that could describe this situation. In each scenario, determine what the probability would be of having a child with freckles and a child without freckles.

To help you figure out this problem, answer the following questions.

(a) Is the freckles allele dominant or recessive? _____
(b) What would be the *three* possible genotypes that a person could have?

Possible Genotypes

(c) What phenotypes would result from each of the three different genotypes?

Genotype	Phenotype

(d) On a separate sheet of paper, use the following Punnett squares to illustrate the two possible scenarios of a woman with freckles and a man without freckles.

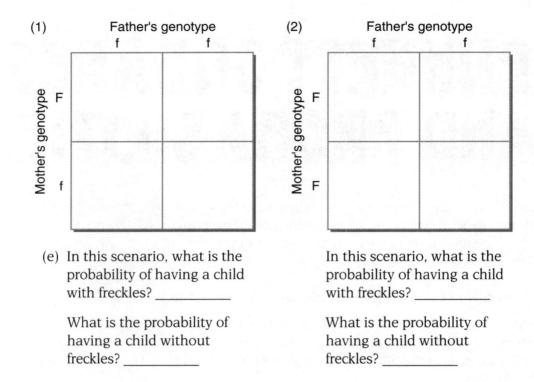

(1)   Father's genotype
         f   f

Mother's genotype   F

                    f

(2)   Father's genotype
         f   f

Mother's genotype   F

                    F

(e) In this scenario, what is the probability of having a child with freckles? _____

What is the probability of having a child without freckles? _____

In this scenario, what is the probability of having a child with freckles? _____

What is the probability of having a child without freckles? _____

Part 2: Predicting the genotypes and phenotypes of the parents

If you know the phenotypes of the offspring, you can make a prediction about the genotypes and phenotypes of the parents.

In this scenario, a mother and a father have two children: one girl and one boy. The girl has freckles; the boy does not. However, the genotypes and phenotypes of the parents are unknown.

(a) What would be the genotype(s) of the girl? _____

(b) What would be the genotype(s) of the boy? _____

(c) Knowing this, what could the genotypes and phenotypes of the parents be? On a separate sheet of paper, complete the following Punnett squares to determine which one(s) could describe the parents. Identify the Punnett squares that could describe this situation.

(1)

Father's genotype

	F	F
F		
F		

Mother's genotype

(2)

Father's genotype

	F	f
F		
F		

Mother's genotype

(3)

Father's genotype

	f	f
F		
F		

Mother's genotype

(4)

Father's genotype

	F	F
F		
f		

Mother's genotype

(5)

Father's genotype

	F	f
F		
f		

Mother's genotype

(6)

Father's genotype

	f	f
F		
f		

Mother's genotype

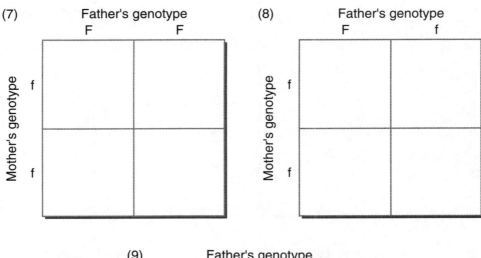

(7) Father's genotype
F   F

Mother's genotype
f
f

(8) Father's genotype
F   f

Mother's genotype
f
f

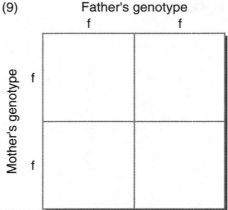

(9) Father's genotype
f   f

Mother's genotype
f
f

(d) Which scenarios could produce one child with freckles and one child without freckles?

(e) In each of those scenarios, what would the genotypes and phenotypes of the parents be? Follow the sample format below:

Scenario # _____

Father's genotype:		Mother's genotype:	
Father's phenotype:		Mother's phenotype:	

(f) Of the possible scenarios that you have listed, explain why the other scenarios could *not* produce both a child with freckles and one without freckles.

(g) Of the possible scenarios that could produce one child with freckles and one child without freckles, can you be certain which one describes this particular situation (without looking at the children's DNA or knowing anything about the parents)? Explain why or why not.

Graphing Skills

Who Is "Dominant" in Your Family?

How are certain traits distributed in your family? Does your family have a lot of people who have dominant traits or recessive traits? Or is there a mix of both? The following chart contains a list of dominant and recessive traits.

1. Conduct a survey to determine which members of your family have either the dominant or the recessive form of the traits listed. You can survey your parents, siblings, grandparents, aunts, uncles, cousins, and so on.

Dominant trait	Number of family members with this trait	Recessive trait	Number of family members with this trait
Brown eyes		Blue eyes	
Freckles		No freckles	
Right handedness		Left handedness	
Can roll tongue		Cannot roll tongue	
Dimples		No dimples	

2. Communicate your results in the form of a bar graph. Recessive traits should be shown in one color and dominant traits in another. Follow the example shown in the bar graph below.

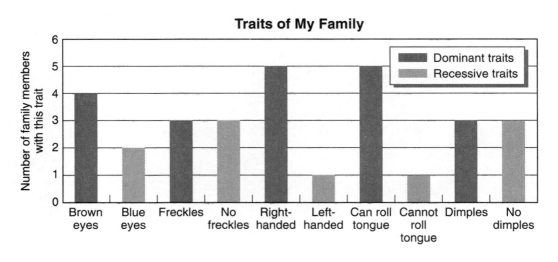

3. On a separate sheet of paper, answer the following questions based on your graph.

   (a) Which traits were the *most* common in your family?

   (b) Which traits were the *least* common in your family?

   (c) Are there more dominant or recessive traits in your family?

   (d) Compare the results of your graph to those of another student in your class. What similarities, if any, did you notice? What differences, if any, did you notice?

   (e) Why do you think there are similarities and/or differences between the data in your graph and the data in your classmate's graph?

   (f) Create your own list of traits (which are *not* already listed in this activity) that are either dominant or recessive. Survey your family members to determine how many of them have those traits.

   (g) Create a bar graph based upon these results (similar to the one you already created for this activity).

PICKING ALLELES TO CREATE A NEW PERSON

The purpose of this activity is to help you learn about how people get their unique looks based on the different combinations of genotypes that they receive from their parents. In this activity, you will work with a partner and each person will represent one of the two parents who contributes genetic information to an organism during fertilization. You will be working with traits that are common.

Part 1

To begin, assign one partner as parent #1 and the other partner as parent #2. **Assume that each person has both a dominant and a recessive allele of each gene** that they could pass on to their offspring. Remember, each parent has two alleles in their genotype (e.g., BB, Bb, or bb) and **there is an equal likelihood of passing down either of the alleles to their offspring**. Each partner will flip a coin to determine which allele they will pass on to the offspring. To determine the gender of your new person, only one partner will flip a coin. A "tails" means the partner contributes a Y chromosome and a "heads" means an X chromosome. For all others, use the key below to determine whether each of you contributes the dominant or recessive allele. On a separate sheet of paper, copy the following chart and enter the results of your coin tosses.

> "Heads" – Dominant allele
> "Tails" – Recessive allele

Trait	Allele Contributed by Person #1	Allele Contributed by Person #2	Phenotype of Person
Female (X) – "Heads" Male (Y) – "Tails"	X*		
Widow's peak – W Straight hair line – w			
Unattached earlobes – E Attached earlobes – e			
Can roll tongue – R Cannot roll tongue – r			
Cleft chin – C Smooth chin – c			
Dimples – D No dimples – d			
Freckles – F No freckles – f			
Brown eyes – B Blue eyes – b			

*Note: The mother always contributes an X chromosome since females never have a Y chromosome.

Part 2

Your next step is to draw what your newly created person's face would look like. Although you did the first part of this activity with a partner, you will each draw the face on your own. To create your drawing, you need to include all of the phenotypes that were determined in Part 1. The other characteristics that were not determined by this activity (hair color, type of hair, shape of nose, etc.) can be decided by you.

Here are five diagrams to help you put together what your new person will look like.

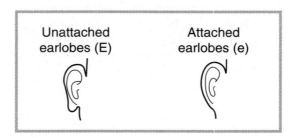

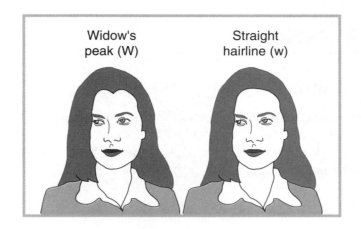

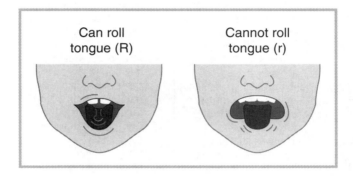

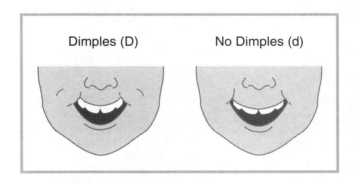

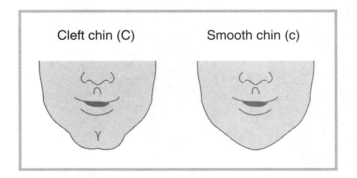

Vocabulary Crossword

Directions: *Each clue below is a definition of one of the vocabulary words that you learned in this chapter. On a printout of the next page provided by your teacher, write the word that matches each definition inside the numbered vertical or horizontal spaces. All the vocabulary words from Chapter 4 are used in this puzzle.*

Across

2. When scientists determine the order of the nitrogen bases of the DNA
3. Mutations that are passed from one generation to a next
8. Variations of a gene
11. The combinations of alleles
14. A person who has an allele for a disease but does not have the disease
16. An allele that will "overpower" the other allele and result in the organism showing that trait
17. A mutation in which a section of the DNA is reversed
18. A mutation in which one or more nitrogen bases are removed from the DNA
19. A chart that shows the possible combinations of alleles that could be created during fertilization
20. A disease that is caused by a mutation in an organism's DNA and may be inherited (although not all are)
21. When scientists look at people's DNA to figure out if they have, or if they are carriers for, a genetic disease
22. A mutation in which one or more nitrogen bases are inserted into the DNA
23. The way that the genotype expresses itself as an observable trait in an organism

Down

1. A mutation in which one nitrogen base has been replaced by another base
4. Mutations that are developed throughout a person's lifetime and are not inherited
5. Companies that use their knowledge of DNA and genes to research genetic diseases and develop medicines to help people with those diseases
6. When people are treated unfairly because of the results of a genetic test
7. A substance that can lead to environmental mutations
8. A genetic disorder that is caused by recessive alleles
9. A genetic disorder that is caused by one dominant allele
10. An allele that can be overpowered by a dominant allele
12. A mistake in the DNA that can result in a trait that is not normal or common
13. A mutation in which the DNA moves because of an insertion or deletion
15. Slight changes that develop in the DNA, which result in common differences in traits within a species

Multiple Choice

For each question, choose the letter of the answer choice that best completes the sentence or answers the question.

1. The condition called albinism is the result of
   a. a mutation   b. a polymorphism   c. the environment   d. smoking

2. Some mutations can be
   a. inside a gene   b. outside a gene   c. fixed by the body   d. all of the above

3. _____ are inherited from one generation to the next.
   a. Germ-line mutations   c. Environmental mutations
   b. Mutagens   d. None of these

4. Mutations can result from
   a. the genes a person inherits   c. tobacco
   b. sunlight   d. all of the above

5. Organisms inherit _____ allele(s) from their parents.
   a. no   b. one   c. two   d. three

6. If "brown eyes" is the dominant trait, then a genotype for brown eyes could be
   a. B   b. b   c. BB   d. bb

7. Tay-Sachs disease can be expressed only if a person inherits _____ recessive alleles.
   a. three   b. two   c. four   d. zero

8. A carrier and a non-carrier of genetic disease have _____ chance of having a child with that disease (if the disease is caused by a recessive allele).
   a. a 100%   b. a 50%   c. a 25%   d. zero

9. Genetic diseases can be
   a. contagious   c. inherited
   b. spread like other diseases d. cured

10. Which of the following genetic diseases is caused by a mutation in a single gene?
    a. cancer   c. Alzheimer's disease
    b. Huntington's disease   d. diabetes

11. Down syndrome is caused by an extra chromosome
    a. 21   b. 17   c. Y   d. X

12. Mutations can happen in
    a. a single gene   b. multiple genes   c. a chromosome   d. all of these

13. There are about _____ different genetic tests available.
  a. 25   b. 100   c. 700   d. 1200

14. Finding the genes that cause diseases requires _____ the DNA of different people.
  a. cloning   b. copying   c. comparing   d. cutting

15. GINA helps protect people against genetic
  a. labeling   b. sequencing   c. discrimination   d. research

True or False

Read each statement and indicate whether it is true or false. If it is false, correct the underlined word(s) to make the statement true.

1. Mutations are mistakes in <u>DNA</u>, which can cause errors in proteins.   1. _____

2. The DNA for brown eyes and the DNA for blue eyes are different types of <u>mutations</u>.   2. _____

3. <u>Environmental mutations</u> get inherited from parents.   3. _____

4. <u>All</u> mutations are harmful.   4. _____

5. Recessive alleles <u>can overpower</u> a dominant allele.   5. _____

6. BB is an example of a <u>genotype</u>.   6. _____

7. A person needs <u>two</u> recessive alleles to have blue eyes.   7. _____

8. It <u>is possible</u> for two carriers of a genetic disease to have a child with that disease.   8. _____

9. <u>All</u> mutations are fatal.   9. _____

10. If two parents are carriers for an autosomal recessive disorder, there is a <u>50%</u> chance of their child having the disease.   10. _____

11. Cystic fibrosis can result in frequent <u>respiratory infections</u>.   11. _____

12. A person can get Huntington's disease if <u>only one parent</u> has the gene for the disease.   12. _____

13. <u>All genetic tests can</u> determine if a person will get a genetic disease.   13. _____

14. <u>All people</u> choose to get genetic testing when they are older.

14. _____

15. Developing a medicine for genetic diseases takes <u>three</u> years.

15. _____

Short Answer

Answer the following questions in one or two complete sentences.

1. Explain why a change in just one nucleotide (nitrogen base) could lead to a protein not working properly.
2. Describe how a mutation arises.
3. Contrast the traits discussed in this chapter that are considered mutations and traits that are considered polymorphisms.
4. Locate the mutations in the following DNA sequences and label them accordingly (on a separate sheet of paper):

	Type of Mutation
1. Original DNA: TACGGTCCAAGA Mutated DNA: TACGGAACCTGA	
2. Original DNA: TACGGTCCAAGA Mutated DNA: TACTGTCCAAGA	
3. Original DNA: TACGGTCCAAGA Mutated DNA: TACGGTAGGCCAAGA	
4. Original DNA: TACGGTCCAAGA Mutated DNA: AGAACCTGGCAT	
5. Original DNA: TACGGTCCAAGA Mutated DNA: TGTCCAAGA	

5. Explain the difference between a trait caused by a dominant allele and a trait caused by a recessive allele.
6. Explain the difference between a genotype and a phenotype. Provide one example of each.
7. Use a Punnett square and explain the chance of having a child with Tay-Sachs disease if only one parent is a carrier of the Tay-Sachs gene.
8. Contrast a genetic disease and a regular disease.
9. What is the difference between diseases like Tay-Sachs disease and Huntington's disease and diseases like cancer and diabetes?
10. What is the difference between an autosomal recessive disorder and an autosomal dominant disorder?
11. Explain why genetic testing is useful.

12. Describe the steps that scientists follow to find a gene that causes a genetic disease.
13. Explain what can be done to help people once the genes that cause a genetic disease have been found.

Going Further

1. Create a poem or song that clears up misconceptions about mutations. Your poem/song should explain what a mutation *is* and is *not*. You might also want to add examples of mutations and tell how biotechnology may help disorders.

2. Imagine you are about to graduate from college and you would like to pursue a job in the biotechnology industry to help people who have genetic diseases. Your teacher will give you a list of some top biotechnology companies and your task is to research three of these companies to decide where you would like to work. Go to each company's Web site to research the information listed below. Once you have collected your information, produce a report along with an explanation of why one of these companies would be your choice for a job.

Information to collect:

- Name of company
- Location of headquarters
- Medical conditions for which they make medicines
- Medical conditions on which they are working (treatments being developed)
- Any other interesting information about the company

Genetic Engineering

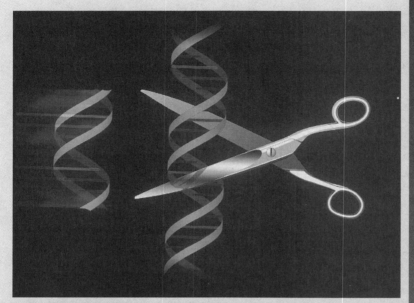

Essential Question:
What are the benefits
and drawbacks of
changing the DNA
of an organism?

Contents

5.1   # What Is Genetic Engineering?

As you have read, biotechnology is the process of using or changing a living thing to improve human lives. Chapters 1 and 2 focused on the many different ways in which people have been using living things to improve their lives, and Chapters 3 and 4 provided you with a background on how DNA functions. Understanding the previous chapters is important for learning how scientists can *change* the DNA of organisms—and why we might even want to do that.

Recall the many different types of disorders that can arise from genetic mutations. What if scientists could try to fix the DNA that was causing those disorders? Think of how people can develop plants and animals with beneficial traits by means of selective breeding. What if researchers could change the DNA of a plant to give it a desired trait, without having to breed as many generations of plants? Scientists use genetic engineering to accomplish these goals. **Genetic engineering** is the process of changing an organism's DNA. This can be done by adding or removing sections of DNA or by turning genes "on" or "off" in an organism. The term *engineering* refers to the process of designing something. For example, different kinds of engineers design machines, buildings, bridges, computers, and so on. In a similar way, *genetic engineers* are scientists who design DNA.

Genetic engineers change particular traits of organisms by making changes to their DNA. Researchers might try to give an organism a new trait or remove a trait it already has. Genetic engineering is a relatively new branch of science. It was first developed in 1973, when two scientists (Stanley Cohen and Herbert Boyer) perfected the technique of changing the DNA of bacteria. The field of genetic engineering has led to ethical debates between people who feel it can help society and others who feel its use should be limited. As you read this chapter, form your own opinions about the possible advantages and disadvantages of genetic engineering.

Exactly how do scientists change the DNA of an organism? Think of a time when you did an art project and you cut out a shape and pasted it onto a picture. This is similar in concept to what genetic engineers do; they cut and "paste" sections of DNA from one organism to another. Generally, the procedure works like this: A scientist identifies the organism that has the desired trait, locates the gene that codes for it, and extracts the DNA. This gene is "designed" to express itself in a specific way (that is, to produce a particular, useful protein). The gene is inserted into bacterial cells (most often) and numerous copies of it are made, thus providing a source for the desired protein. Specifically, the steps are:

1. The gene the researcher *identifies* could come from any organism, usually different from the species that is to receive the new section of DNA. Scientists compare the DNA of organisms with different traits in order to find a specific gene that produces the desired trait (or protein).

2. Once they find the gene they want, scientists *cut out* the section of DNA that contains it by using a *restriction enzyme*. **Restriction enzymes** are proteins that will cut the DNA at very specific places. Think of restriction enzymes as "smart scissors" that will recognize and cut only certain items. More than 3800 restriction enzymes have been identified; so scientists have a large selection of enzymes from which to pick the one that

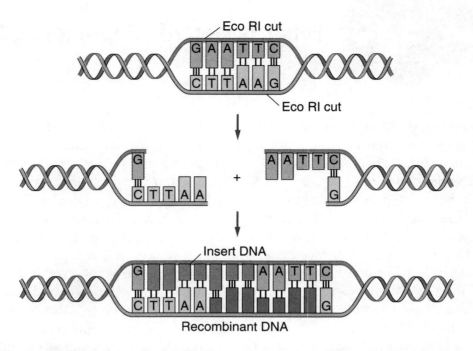

Eco RI cut

G A A T T C
C T T A A G

Eco RI cut

G + A A T T C
C T T A A   G

Insert DNA

G   A A T T C
C T T A A   G

Recombinant DNA

Figure 5-1. The action of a restriction enzyme: The original double strand of DNA is cut and another piece of DNA with the desired trait is spliced into the DNA strands.

will cut the right section of DNA with the desired gene. (See Figure 5-1.)

3. Once the DNA is cut, the researchers insert, or *splice*, the new desirable gene into the DNA of a **vector** (a transporter of DNA), which is usually a bacterial plasmid or a virus. (A *plasmid* is a small circular piece of DNA that can replicate on its own. A *virus* is a particle of genetic material that can replicate only within another living cell.) **Gene splicing** is the process of joining one section of DNA with another. The bacterial or viral vector is needed for the process because either can replicate the DNA that has received the new desirable gene. In the case of bacteria, the gene is replicated every time the bacteria replicate and divide. In the case of viruses, the gene can be expressed when the virus reproduces its DNA within a host cell. (See Figure 5-2.)

4. Last, the scientists can *transport* the vector into the organism that they want

to change. The vectors are able to enter into the other organism's cells, replicate their DNA (with the new gene in it), and thereby express the gene and produce more of the protein for which it codes. The vector incorporates its DNA into that of the organism, which results in a new, genetically engineered organism.

The new DNA that is created from gene splicing is called **recombinant DNA**, which is why genetic engineering is sometimes referred to as *recombinant DNA technology*. Recombinant DNA can be thought of as a new combination of DNA that was developed by scientists. When looking at the word recombinant, note that the prefix *re* means "again" or "anew"; and you can see that the word *combination* is related to the term recombinant. Put these ideas together and you can think of recombinant DNA as a new combination of DNA that has been created by scientists. When recombinant DNA is created, the organism that results is called a *transgenic organism.*

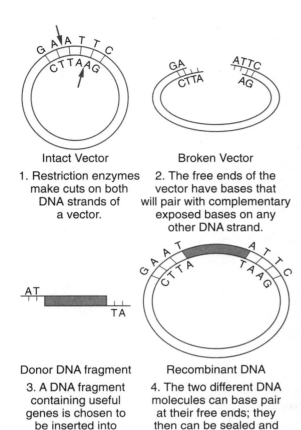

Intact Vector

1. Restriction enzymes make cuts on both DNA strands of a vector.

Broken Vector

2. The free ends of the vector have bases that will pair with complementary exposed bases on any other DNA strand.

Donor DNA fragment

3. A DNA fragment containing useful genes is chosen to be inserted into this vector.

Recombinant DNA

4. The two different DNA molecules can base pair at their free ends; they then can be sealed and inserted into a bacterial cell.

Figure 5-2. Scientists use vectors, such as circular pieces of bacterial DNA, to insert and move genes from one organism to another. The vector is usually placed within a bacterial cell, where it can reproduce quickly and make more copies of the new DNA.

Thus, a **transgenic organism** is one that has had *genes* from a different kind of organism *transferred* into its DNA.

The purpose of genetic engineering is to create an organism with a new trait, and in that sense it is similar to selective breeding. There are, however, two main differences. Selective breeding can take many generations to create an organism with a desired trait. With genetic engineering, a scientist usually needs much less time to accomplish that task because they can transfer the gene for that trait to the organism. The other difference is that, with genetic engineering, a scientist could theoretically take a gene from any species to put in an organism. With selective breeding, scientists are limited to genes from the same species.

Genetic engineering opens up a world of possibilities for scientists. It also opens up a debate about the ethics of changing an organism's DNA. In the next few sections, you will read about how scientists use genetic engineering to make medicines from bacteria; alter the traits of some crops we commonly eat; try to cure people of genetic diseases; and consider the pros (benefits) and/or cons (harm) in trying to genetically alter a person's traits.

Lesson 5.1 Review

Vocabulary Check

For each of the following terms, give a complete definition.

1. Genetic engineering

2. Restriction enzymes

3. Vector

4. Gene splicing

5. Recombinant DNA

6. Transgenic organism

Multiple Choice

For each question, choose the letter of the answer choice that best completes the sentence or answers the question.

1. Genetic engineering can be done by
   a. adding DNA   b. removing DNA   c. turning genes "on"   d. all of the above

2. Genetic engineering was first developed in
   a. 1937   b. 1967   c. 1973   d. 1976

3. The first organism to be genetically engineered was a
   a. bacterium   b. plant   c. chimpanzee   d. human

4. The first step in genetic engineering is to _____ the gene with a desired trait.
   a. locate   b. cut   c. create   d. destroy

5. Restriction enzymes are similar in concept to
   a. tape   b. glue   c. scissors   d. paper

6. The prefix "re" means
   a. after   b. anew   c. first   d. last

7. Which of these is used as a vector to insert new DNA into an organism?
   a. enzymes   b. yeast   c. viruses   d. plants

8. Genetic engineering is most similar to which of these?
   a. selective breeding   b. fermentation   c. bioremediation   d. composting

True or False

Read each statement and indicate whether it is true or false. If it is false, correct the underlined word(s) to make the statement true.

1. A genetic engineer can be thought of as someone who designs <u>buildings</u>.

1. _____

2. The purpose of genetic engineering is to <u>change</u> a trait in an organism.

2. _____

3. There is a lot of <u>agreement</u> about genetic engineering.

3. _____

4. Restriction enzymes <u>glue DNA together</u>.

4. _____

5. DNA <u>can be</u> directly inserted into an organism.

5. _____

6. Recombinant DNA creates a <u>transgenic organism</u>.

6. _____

7. With genetic engineering, scientists can <u>use genes from only the same species</u> of organism.

7. _____

Short Answer

Answer the following questions in one or two complete sentences.

1. Explain how an organism can be genetically engineered (in other words, what can scientists do to its DNA?).
2. How is genetic engineering similar in concept to other types of engineering?
3. Briefly describe the *four* steps that scientists take to change an organism's DNA.
4. (a) List the two types of vectors that are often used during genetic engineering. (b) Describe why vectors are used to make recombinant DNA.
5. Compare and contrast genetic engineering and selective breeding. Give *one* similarity and *two* differences.

Going Further

1. Draw a diagram that shows the four steps of genetic engineering. Your pictures should clearly illustrate and label each step of the process.

2. Analogies are used to compare two things that are otherwise not similar; they can be useful in trying to learn new concepts. One example used in this lesson is that restriction enzymes are like scissors, because they can cut DNA. Work with a partner to think of an analogy for each of the vocabulary terms in this section. Explain why each word is a good analogy for the vocabulary term. *Optional*: Illustrate each vocabulary term with a picture of the word to which it is similar.

How Can Bacteria Be Used to Make Medicines?

Up until the 1970s, people had been only *using* living things to do something beneficial, which is often called *classical biotechnology.* This all changed in 1973 when a geneticist named Stanley Cohen (1935–) and a biochemist named Herbert Boyer (1936–) first figured out how to *change* a living thing to make it do something beneficial. Working together, Cohen and Boyer were able to change the DNA of a strain of bacteria called *Escherichia coli* (*E. coli*), which are normally found within our intestines and are important for healthy functioning. Some strains of *E. coli* can make a person sick if ingested, so you might think these bacteria are harmful. Yet it was the unique abilities of this bacterium that led to a change in medical uses of biotechnology, starting what is now called *modern biotechnology.*

So why were Boyer and Cohen's experiments so important? They figured out how to change the DNA of *E. coli* so that it could make human insulin. **Human insulin** is a hormone (a protein) produced by the pancreas gland after a person has eaten, increasing levels of glucose (sugar) in the blood. Glucose is needed to provide energy to cells. However, too much or too little glucose in the blood can be harmful. The insulin signals liver, fat, and muscle cells to remove the excess glucose, thus ensuring a stable blood sugar level. (See Figure 5-3.)

Diabetes is a condition that results in excess glucose (blood sugar) levels in the body due to an inability of the pancreas to produce sufficient insulin. The need to engineer bacterial cells to make insulin comes from the growing number of people with diabetes, particularly Type 2 diabetes. Type 1, formerly called *juvenile*, diabetes starts at an early age; the body produces little to no insulin. Type 2, also called *adult-onset*, diabetes occurs when the body does produce insulin but the cells are not able to use it as well as they should. If untreated, excess blood sugar levels from diabetes can lead to major health problems, such as eye, kidney, and heart ailments. This is a serious situation because diabetes is growing at an alarming rate; in fact, one new case is diagnosed every five seconds. Sadly, half the people with diabetes do not know they have the disease.

Giving insulin to people who have diabetes can help them control their blood-sugar level, which is how biotechnology can help. Scientists can take a cell from a healthy person and remove the gene that has the instructions to make insulin. Then, they splice that gene into the DNA of the *E. coli* bacterial cell. As mentioned in the four steps, the type of bacterial DNA they work with is a **plasmid**, the loop of DNA that is separate from the bacterium's main DNA. Plasmids are ideal for genetic engineering because of their circular shape—it is relatively simple for scientists to

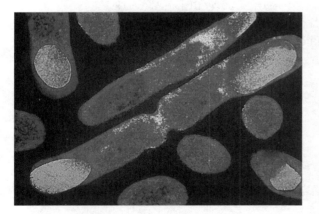

Figure 5-3. Boyer and Cohen figured out how to change the DNA of *E. coli* so that it could make human insulin. These *E. coli* bacteria have been genetically engineered to produce human insulin. *Note:* The areas that produce insulin glow.

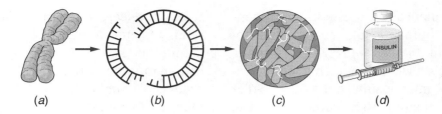

Figure 5-4. The insulin gene is inserted into bacterial plasmids. The bacteria that contain this gene produce insulin, which is used by people with diabetes.

cut open the DNA and paste in the new gene. (See Figure 5-4.)

After the bacterial cell has a new gene inserted into it, it is kept in a **bioreactor**, a machine that provides the ideal temperature and nutrients to allow the bacteria to grow and multiply many times. Once there are enough bacterial cells, the insulin they produce is separated from the bacteria by purification methods. (See Figure 5-5.)

In 1982, the Food and Drug Administration (FDA) approved the first genetically engineered insulin to be sold. This was deve-

loped by the first biotechnology company, called *Genentech* (which was co-founded by Herbert Boyer). Scientists continue to look for innovative ways to engineer an organism to make human insulin. There are currently clinical trials being run by a Canadian biotechnology company to test insulin from a genetically engineered safflower (a type of flower), but that form of insulin has yet to be approved for people by the FDA. If approved, this type of insulin may be cheaper to produce, making it more affordable for patients who need it.

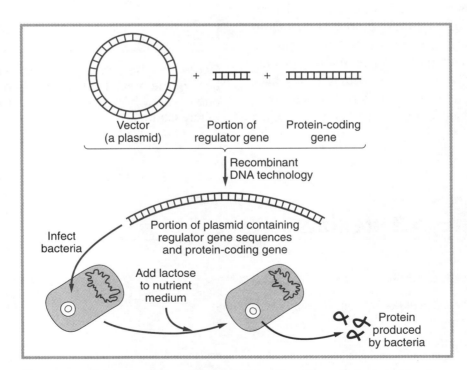

Figure 5-5. Scientists use a bioreactor to allow the engineered bacteria to multiply many times and produce more of the needed proteins, such as insulin.

Why is genetically engineering an organism to make human insulin such a huge development in biotechnology? For starters, before scientists were able to engineer bacteria to make human insulin, patients with diabetes used insulin that came from the pancreases of other mammals, such as cows and pigs. However, there is a limited amount of animal-derived insulin, which leads to increased cost. In addition, although pig insulin protein is very close to that of humans, it is still different enough to cause medical problems in some people. So, insulin from genetically engineered bacteria is most compatible for use by other humans because it comes from human genes. Also, there is a potentially unlimited supply, which keeps the insulin more affordable.

Insulin is not the only example of a medicine that can be produced for people through biotechnology. Another protein that has been made through genetically engineered bacteria is human growth hormone. **Human growth hormone** (**hGH**) is a protein that controls growth in the human body and is secreted from the pituitary gland. The *pituitary gland*, located in the center of the brain, is sometimes called the "master gland" because it controls other glands and releases hormones that affect many different functions in the body. (See Figure 5-6.) People's bodies typically release hGH throughout their lifetime, peaking during adolescence, then declining afterward. Sometimes, because of certain mutations in their DNA, people do not produce enough hGH, so their bones and muscles do not get the signal to grow. As a result, this lack of sufficient hGH causes people to be unusually short. However, with treatments of hGH they might be able to grow to a normal height. In 1985, the FDA approved hGH to be given to people with growth hormone deficiencies, making it the second medicine that is made from genetically engineered *E. coli* bacteria.

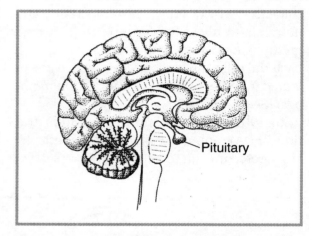

Figure 5-6. **The pituitary gland is located at the base of the brain. Human growth hormone is one of many hormones secreted from the pituitary gland.**

Lesson 5.2 Review

Vocabulary Check

For each of the following terms, give a complete definition.

1. Human insulin
2. Plasmid
3. Bioreactor
4. Human growth hormone (hGH)

Multiple Choice

For each question, choose the letter of the answer choice that best completes the sentence or answers the question.

1. The bacterium used to make insulin and human growth hormone is
   a. *P. shermanii*   b. *E. coli*   c. *S. cerevisiae*   d. *P. notatum*

2. Insulin is produced in the
   a. stomach   b. liver   c. pancreas   d. muscles

3. One new case of diabetes is diagnosed every
   a. 5 seconds   b. 10 minutes   c. 5 hours   d. day

4. Untreated diabetes could lead to problems of the
   a. eye   b. kidney   c. heart   d. all of these

5. In _____, the FDA approved the first genetically engineered insulin to be sold.
   a. 1973   b. 1975   c. 1982   d. 1985

6. The animal that has an insulin protein that is closest to that of humans is the
   a. cow   b. pig   c. sheep   d. duck

7. The hormone that controls people's growth is produced in the
   a. liver   b. heart   c. stomach   d. brain

True or False

Read each statement and indicate whether it is true or false. If it is false, correct the underlined word(s) to make the statement true.

1. When scientists figured out how to change the DNA of bacteria to make a medicine, this started <u>classic biotechnology</u>.

   1. _____

2. With <u>Type 1 diabetes</u>, the body does produce insulin but it does not use insulin as well as it should.

   2. _____

3. <u>Half the</u> people with diabetes do not even know they have the condition.

   3. _____

4. There are currently clinical trials to test insulin made from a genetically engineered <u>tree</u>.

   4. _____

5. Human growth hormone typically peaks during <u>adolescence</u>.

   5. _____

6. The second genetically engineered medicine was <u>insulin</u>.

   6. _____

Short Answer

Answer the following questions in one or two complete sentences.

1. Explain the difference between classical and modern biotechnology.
2. Explain the role of insulin in our bodies.
3. Describe how scientists can produce insulin from *E. coli* bacteria (include the role of the bioreactor in making this happen).
4. Describe *two* advantages that insulin from genetically modified bacteria has over insulin taken from pigs or cows.
5. (a) Describe what happens to people when their bodies do not release enough hGH. (b) Explain how biotechnology can help them.

Going Further

1. Genentech is one of the founding biotechnology companies. It was founded in part by Herbert Boyer who, along with Stanley Cohen, discovered how to carry out genetic engineering in a bacterial cell. Working on your own or with a partner, research and write a brochure on the history of Genentech (a division of Roche) that summarizes information about its founders and major developments. Highlight important developments the company has made since it was founded in 1976. Focus on major awards that Genentech has received and medicines that they have developed (which have been approved by the FDA). Your brochure will be graded according to the rubric given by your teacher.

   Use the company Web site to find this information:

   http://www.gene.com/gene/about/corporate/history/timeline.html
   http://www.gene.com/gene/about/corporate/history/founders.html

2. Research the work that has been done by the French pharmaceutical company *Sanofi-Aventis*, which has engineered a strain of yeast to produce the anti-malarial drug artemisinin. Discuss when and how this medication will be approved for use by the public.

3. Research the work being done by the San Francisco-based biotech company *LS9 Inc.* to bioengineer *E. coli* to mass-produce a diesel-like form of fuel by giving the bacteria genes from blue-green algae that naturally make the fuel.

Lesson 5.3   How Does Gene Therapy Help People?

Think back to the genetic diseases and disorders you read about in Chapter 3. You learned that some diseases are caused by mutations in DNA, either from mutations that someone is born with or from mutations that happen over time (as with some cancers). Currently, there are no FDA-approved cures for these genetic diseases. However, scientists are trying to use a new method, called *gene therapy*, to cure genetic disorders. **Gene therapy** is a technique that aims to fix the mutations in a person's DNA that can cause a genetic disease. The theory behind gene therapy is that, if normal DNA is received into the body, it will do the work that the missing or defective DNA was not able to do.

To change someone's DNA, scientists do not remove a bad gene from the person. The mutation is in every cell of a person's body, so there is no way for scientists to take that gene out of every one of his or her cells. However, there are two methods by which scientists can give a person the new DNA: *in vivo* or *in vitro*. **In vivo** is a Latin term that means "in the living"; thus the scientists carry out a procedure directly in the body. **In vitro** is a Latin term that means "in glass"; thus the scientists carry out the procedure in a test tube or petri dish.

In vivo gene therapy is carried out by means of a **direct gene transfer**.

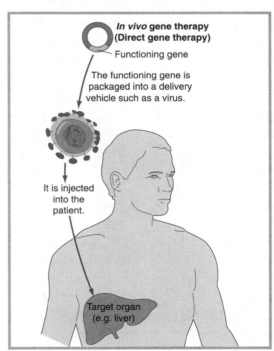

Figure 5-7. With in vivo, or direct, gene therapy, vectors are used to transport the functioning gene directly into a person's body.

In vivo gene therapy (Direct gene therapy)
Functioning gene
The functioning gene is packaged into a delivery vehicle such as a virus.
It is injected into the patient.
Target organ (e.g. liver)

In this technique, vectors are used to transport the functioning gene directly into a person's body. It is a relatively simple way to give the person the genes that he or she needs. Scientists have to use a vector to introduce the new DNA because it is very difficult to insert DNA directly into a person's body. The most common vectors used are genetically engineered viruses (particles of genetic material) that have been given the normal gene that the patient needs. (See Figure 5-7.)

There are a few different types of viruses that scientists can use to transfer a gene, depending on what type of cells they would like to change. As stated above, viruses have the ability to enter cells and insert their DNA into that of the host organism. Although an advantage of this method is that it is simple, a disadvantage is that it is not very accurate. The viruses might not enter the correct tissue or organ and, even if they do, they might not insert the new gene into the correct location in the person's DNA. If the new gene is inserted into a wrong location, it could create other health problems, especially if it is inserted in the middle of another gene, which could alter its function).

In vitro gene therapy is a more complex method for changing a person's DNA. The advantage with this method is that scientists

---

Genetic Engineering   **151**

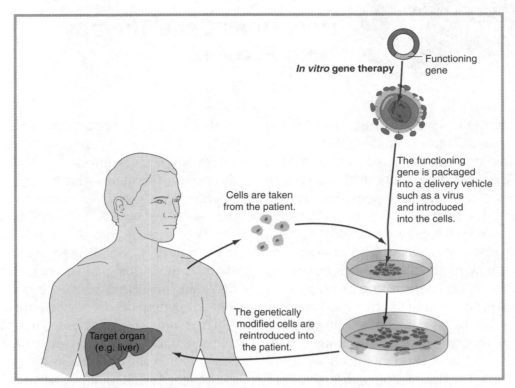

Figure 5-8. With in vitro gene therapy, cells are taken from the patient, genetically modified, and then reintroduced into the patient's body.

have more control over where the new gene goes in the person's body; that is, they can insert the new gene into a specific spot within a person's DNA. In vitro gene therapy is done by taking cells from the patient and keeping those cells alive in a petri dish. Then the new gene is introduced into those cells by means of a genetically engineered virus. After the virus has changed the DNA of those cells, they are reintroduced back into the person's body, right into the body part where the scientists want the new gene to make its protein. The disadvantage of this method is that it is very difficult to keep cells alive outside the body for a long time. (See Figure 5-8.)

Gene therapy is still a very new and experimental approach to treating genetic disorders. Since the first gene therapy trial began in 1990, there have been some successes as well as some setbacks. In that year, a girl named Ashanti de Silva became the first patient to be treated with gene therapy in an effort to treat a disease she had inherited called

ADA deficiency. ADA deficiency is a genetic disease in which the body lacks an enzyme necessary for proper immune function. As a result, patients with ADA deficiency are often prone to many infections. Because of the gene therapy she received, Ashanti is still alive and healthy today. Since that first use of gene therapy, it has been used as an experimental procedure to try to treat other genetic diseases, such as cystic fibrosis and cancer. In 2009, researchers announced that, through gene therapy, they had successfully treated color blindness in monkeys, which could one day lead to a cure for people with that disorder. (See Figure 5-9.)

For all its successes, however, there have been some problems with gene therapy. In 1999, the first death of a patient occurred that resulted from the experimental use of gene therapy. In 2003, the FDA put a ban on gene therapy after it was learned that some patients who had undergone the treatment later developed a leukemia-like disease. The ban, however, was later eased. Because of its experimental nature, gene therapy has not yet been approved by the FDA as a treatment for genetic diseases. Currently, the only way for someone to receive gene therapy is to be involved in a clinical trial.

One problem with gene therapy is the high cost of the technique, which might make it available only for those patients who can afford it. Another concern is that gene therapy only *fixes* the problem in the person, but does not *prevent* the mutation from being passed on to that person's offspring. In other words, the patient will still have the mutations in his or her reproductive cells.

Figure 5-9. Since 1990, gene therapy treatment has been used as an experimental procedure to try to treat genetic diseases, such as cystic fibrosis and cancer. Here, a young cystic fibrosis patient is receiving a less permanent form of treatment, percussion (to loosen mucus in the lungs) by a physiotherapist.

One more concern some people may have is that gene therapy could be used to change parts of a person's DNA for reasons unrelated to genetic defects and medical need. For example, it is feared that the technique could be used to change DNA just to give people some new desirable traits, such as a different eye color, or to rid people of traits that are considered undesirable (but not life-threatening). The risk is that it may become unclear whether certain traits are true disorders (and therefore should be changed to save lives) or simply undesirable traits that really do not negatively affect a person's life. This concept will be further discussed later in the chapter.

Lesson 5.3 Review

Vocabulary Check

For each of the following terms, give a complete definition.

1. Gene therapy

2. In vivo

3. In vitro

4. Direct gene transfer

Multiple Choice

For each question, choose the letter of the answer choice that best completes the sentence or answers the question.

1. Currently, there are _____ cures for genetic diseases that have been approved by the FDA.
   a. no   b. two   c. some   d. many

2. Experiments done in vitro are done in a(n)
   a. body   b. plant   c. animal   d. dish

3. The most common vectors used in gene therapy are
   a. bacteria   b. viruses   c. people   d. liposomes

4. The first gene therapy trial on a person was carried out in
   a. 1990   b. 1999   c. 2003   d. 2009

5. The first genetic disease to be treated using gene therapy was
   a. cancer   b. cystic fibrosis   c. ADA deficiency   d. color blindness

True or False

Read each statement and indicate whether it is true or false. If it is false, correct the underlined word(s) to make the statement true.

1. The idea behind gene therapy is that the <u>normal DNA</u> will do the work of the missing or defective DNA.

   1. _____

2. To change someone's DNA, scientists <u>remove a bad gene from</u> a person.

   2. _____

3. Viruses <u>have the ability</u> to change the DNA of an organism.

   3. _____

4. In vitro gene therapy is <u>less complex</u> than in vivo gene therapy.

   4. _____

5. Gene therapy is a <u>very old</u> approach to treating genetic disorders.

   5. _____

6. There have been <u>some problems</u> with gene therapy.

   6. _____

7. Currently, the only way to get gene therapy is to be involved in <u>a clinical trial</u>.

   7. _____

Short Answer

Answer the following questions in one or two complete sentences.

1. Explain how scientists can give a person new DNA by the in vivo method.
2. Explain how scientists can give someone new DNA in vitro (in *three* steps).
3. Evaluate the advantages and disadvantages of doing in vivo and in vitro gene therapy.
4. (a) Describe what happens to a person with ADA deficiency. (b) Explain what happened to the first patient of a gene therapy experiment.
5. Discuss *three* concerns people have about gene therapy.
6. Justify why you think gene therapy is a good idea or a bad idea. Explain why you feel this way.

Going Further

Working with a partner, create an informational poster about how people can use genetic engineering (through both genetically engineered bacteria and gene therapy) to improve their health. In your poster, include the following information:

- A description of each method (creating genetically modified bacteria and carrying out gene therapy)
- An explanation of how scientists create genetically modified bacteria and of how scientists perform gene therapy
- An explanation of why scientists would want to use these treatments instead of traditional medicines (if any exist)
- The type of conditions that each treatment is aiming to help

Your poster will be graded according to the rubric provided by your teacher.

Do You Eat Genetically Modified Foods?

Would you feel comfortable eating a food if you knew its DNA had been changed by scientists? What if you were told the food was safe and there were many benefits? The truth is, you most likely have already eaten foods that have had their DNA changed and probably not even realized it. Some people would say that **genetically modified (GM) foods**, food plants and animals that have had their DNA changed by scientists, are very beneficial. Others would argue that more research needs to be done on these types of foods. This section will explain the potential benefits and also the concerns about changing the DNA of the foods we eat. You can determine for yourself how you feel about *agricultural biotechnology*, that is, the biotechnology related to plants and animals developed for human uses. (See Figure 5-10.)

In 1994, the first GM food was approved for human consumption by the FDA; it was called the *Flavr Savr* tomato. This tomato was genetically engineered to stay firm after harvest, which would allow it to last longer on the vine before shipping. The tomatoes were

Figure 5-11. The first genetically modified (GM) food that was approved by the FDA for human consumption was the *Flavr Savr* tomato. Here a scientist is examining a tomato in her lab.

not labeled as genetically modified, so consumers were unaware of any changes. However, the *Flavr Savr* tomato was too costly to produce and, as a result, did not last long on the market. (See Figure 5-11.)

Although the idea of changing the characteristics of foods seems new, it is not. Remember, people have been "designing" foods for thousands of years by using selective breeding to develop desired traits. However, unlike selective breeding, the use of genetic engineering to create GM foods allows scientists to potentially use genes from *any* species. Why would scientists want to change the DNA of food? GM foods are created because the scientists believe that the modified food would be beneficial to either the farmers who grow it or the people who consume it. Most GM foods developed and used today are created to improve the quality of the food. For example, the three traits that are most commonly engineered into crops are those that make the food plant resistant to insects, tolerant (accepting) of chemical herbicides, and/or resistant to viruses.

Figure 5-10. Many grocery store items may be genetically modified; in fact, you have probably eaten foods that have had their DNA changed and not even known it.

Making plants resistant to insects is beneficial to the farmers because insects can be devastating to crops. If plant foods have a gene in them that makes them resistant to insects, farmers would not have to spray their crops with **insecticides** (types of *pesticides*), the chemicals that can kill insects. (See Figure 5-12.) These insecticides can be very dangerous to handle, so farmers would benefit by being able to avoid working with these chemicals (and consumers would not have to eat plants that had been sprayed with them). One example of this is the genetically modified corn called *Bt corn*. This corn was developed by taking a gene from a soil bacterium called *Bacillus thuringiensis*, or *Bt* (which produces a toxin to an insect called the European corn borer caterpillar), and inserting it into the DNA of corn. The Bt toxin is harmful only to caterpillars, not to the people who eat the corn.

Figure 5-12. **If crops receive a gene that makes them resistant to insects, farmers would not have to spray the plants with insecticides, which can be harmful for farmers to handle and for consumers to eat. Here a worker is wearing a protective mask while he sprays a strawberry field with a pesticide.**

Farmers can also benefit from growing crops with a gene that makes them tolerant of herbicides; they could spray herbicides on their crops without worrying about damaging the food plants. **Herbicides** are chemicals used to kill weeds that can harm crops. The problem is that herbicides are not selective and they can hurt all plants, including the ones the farmer is trying to grow. If the GM plants are tolerant of herbicides, then they could be sprayed to kill any

Figure 5-13. **Scientists are trying to engineer foods that can fight health problems, such as a new type of banana that has a gene for a hepatitis B vaccine.**

surrounding weeds without damaging the crops. One example of this is called the *Roundup Ready soybean*. This soybean was engineered by an agricultural biotechnology company so that farmers could spray the soybeans with their herbicide (called *Roundup*) without damaging the soybean crop.

Since plants can get viruses that can make them spoil, it would be beneficial to engineer crops with a gene that makes them resistant to viral infections. This idea was put to use in Hawaii in the late 1990s when there was an outbreak of the papaya ringspot virus and the papaya crops were decreased. Once the GM papaya (called *SunUp* or *Rainbow papaya*) was introduced, which had a gene that was resistant to the virus, the papaya crops increased again.

These three examples are not the only traits that are modified in food organisms. Another example of a genetically modified food being developed includes a salmon that now contains a growth hormone gene from a different type of salmon, which helps it grow in half the time it normally takes to mature. Also, efforts are underway to tackle two major health problems (hepatitis B and blindness) in developing nations. One plan is to engineer a type of banana that has a gene for a hepatitis B vaccine. (See Figure 5-13.) The other plan is to develop a variety of rice (called *Golden Rice*) that has a gene to make extra Vitamin A, to help prevent blindness. Scientists are currently developing the transgenic *Enviropig*, which has been given a gene from *E. coli* called *phytase*. The gene codes for an enzyme that aids digestion of a specific nutrient; so the pig eats less food, produces less waste, and, as a result, causes less contamination of agricultural areas. These are just some of the foods that scientists are working on modifying, but they have yet to be approved to be sold to people to eat.

Today, it is estimated that between 70 and 85 percent of the foods we eat have ingredients that have been genetically modified. The most common foods that have had their DNA changed include corn and soybeans (which together make up about 84 percent of GM foods worldwide). Other crops that have been modified include canola, cotton, rice, sugar beets, potatoes, tomatoes, squash, papaya, and flax. Ingredients made from GM soybeans can be found in many processed foods. Since 93 percent of the soy that is planted in the United States is genetically modified, it is very likely that you have eaten foods with GM ingredients (such as soy oil and lecithin). You probably did not know this because there are no laws in this country requiring that GM foods be labeled as such.

As with other forms of genetic engineering, scientists have to first find an organism that has the desired gene to be inserted into the DNA of a plant or an animal. Livestock can be modified by using the techniques similar to those used during gene therapy. One way that genetically modified crops are developed is by using a tool called a *gene gun*. A **gene gun** is a machine that shoots gene-coated pellets through the cells of a plant in order to introduce a new gene to that plant. Scientists put a group of **undifferentiated cells** (that is, cells which have not become specialized) from a plant onto a petri dish. The gene gun blasts the gene-coated pellets at the plant cells and, as the pellets pass into them, the desired gene becomes integrated into the DNA of some of the cells. These cells are then grown into a full plant that has modified DNA. (See Figure 5-14.)

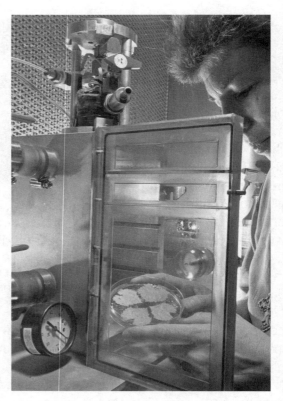

Figure 5-14. A gene gun shoots gene-coated pellets into a plant's cells to introduce a new gene. Here a gene gun is being prepared to shoot genes into grape leaves.

The other way in which plants can have their DNA changed is through the use of a bacterial species called *Agrobacterium tumefaciens*. This bacterium is used because it has the ability to change the DNA of plant cells. Scientists can splice the gene desired for the plant into the DNA of *A. tumefaciens* bacterial cells. Next they place these cells in a petri dish with undifferentiated plant cells; the bacteria would then transfer their modified genes into the plant cells.

As with many aspects of modern biotechnology, there are some controversies about GM foods. People may think that by creating GM foods, we are tampering with nature. However, the two main concerns that some people have about GM foods are that they could be harmful to people *and* to other organisms. For people, the concern is that GM foods could cause a bad reaction when eaten if it has a gene from a different food to which a person is allergic. This concern was the result of a report by scientists stating that a gene from the Brazil nut was put into the DNA of a soybean (to boost its nutritional content). The Brazil nut, like the peanut, is known to cause allergic reactions in some people. The report stated that the GM soybean was producing proteins that might cause allergic reactions in people who had a Brazil-nut allergy. Fortunately, this soybean variety was never sold, but the fear of allergic reactions remained. Yet, a report by scientists in 2005 stated that to date, no GM foods have produced any proteins that could cause allergic reactions. (See Figure 5-15.)

The other main concern about GM foods is that they will be harmful to other organisms. This concern stemmed from a 1999 report stating that the pollen from genetically modified Bt corn could potentially kill monarch butterflies. Milkweed, the plant that monarch butterfly caterpillars feed on, grows mostly around cornfields; so researchers were concerned that the pollen from GM corn would land on the milkweed plants and harm the caterpillars. In their laboratory experiments, the scientists sprinkled Bt corn pollen on milkweed leaves and allowed the caterpillars to eat the leaves. They found that the caterpillars ate less, grew more slowly, and died at a higher rate than caterpillars that did not have Bt pollen on their milkweed. However, the EPA has now concluded that Bt corn is *not* harmful to monarch caterpillars under normal field conditions. The EPA claims that the amount of Bt pollen put on the leaves by researchers was significantly higher than the amount that would naturally occur in a field; not all monarch caterpillars eat milkweed near cornfields anyway. (See Figure 5-16.)

Figure 5-16. Researchers were concerned that pollen from GM corn would land on nearby milkweed plants and harm the monarch caterpillars that feed on them; fortunately, the GM corn is not harmful to monarch caterpillars out in the field.

Clearly, the ability to bio-engineer our crops and livestock presents as much food for *thought* as it does for our tables! There are both benefits and possible drawbacks to changing some genetic traits of the plants and animals we consume. As a consumer, it is up to you to decide if you agree or disagree with the development of new types of genetically modified foods.

Figure 5-15. People were concerned when a gene from the Brazil nut (top), which is known to cause allergic reactions in some people, was put into the DNA of a soybean (bottom); so this variety of GM soybean was never sold.

Lesson 5.4 Review

Vocabulary Check

For each of the following terms, give a complete definition.

1. Genetically modified (GM) foods

2. Insecticides

3. Herbicides

4. Gene gun

5. Undifferentiated cells

Multiple Choice

For each question, choose the letter of the answer choice that best completes the sentence or answers the question.

1. The first genetically modified food was approved in
   a. 1904   b. 1994   c. 2000   d. 2004

2. Which of the following traits is *not* the most common one in GM foods?
   a. stay fresh longer   c. resist insects
   b. tolerate herbicides   d. resist viruses

3. The Bt corn was engineered to have a gene from
   a. tomatoes   b. bacteria   c. cows   d. bananas

4. One animal that has been modified to grow at double its normal rate is a
   a. cow   b. pig   c. salmon   d. chicken

5. It is estimated that about _____ percent of foods have GM ingredients in them.
   a. 20−35   b. 45−60   c. 70−85   d. 90−100

6. Besides the use of a gene gun, GM plants can be created by using
   a. *A. tumefaciens*   b. *B. thuringiensis*   c. fungi   d. viruses

7. People were concerned about possible allergic reactions to GM soybeans that contained a gene from
   a. tomatoes   b. bacteria   c. caterpillars   d. Brazil nuts

8. Scientists have concluded that, in the field, Bt corn is _____ harmful to nearby monarch butterfly caterpillars.
   a. usually   b. sometimes   c. very   d. not at all

True or False

Read each statement and indicate whether it is true or false. If it is false, correct the underlined word(s) to make the statement true.

1. Genetically modified foods can be <u>plants or animals</u>.

2. The first GM food that was approved was a type of <u>corn</u>.

3. Changing the characteristics of food <u>is a new idea</u>.

4. People were concerned about allergic reactions to <u>GM peanuts</u>.

5. Golden Rice is a GM food that was developed to help prevent <u>bacterial infections</u>.

6. It is <u>not likely</u> that a person in the U.S. has eaten a GM food.

7. In the U.S., there are <u>no laws</u> that require GM foods to be labeled.

8. A 1999 report claimed that Bt corn might be harmful to <u>people.</u>

1. _____

2. _____

3. _____

4. _____

5. _____

6. _____

7. _____

8. _____

Short Answer

Answer the following questions in one or two complete sentences.

1. Explain why the idea of modifying foods is not a new idea.

2. (a) Describe why farmers would want to grow crops that are tolerant of herbicides and resistant to insects and/or viruses. (b) For each of the following traits listed, name a GM food that was engineered to have that trait: (1) tolerant of herbicides; (2) resistant to insects; and (3) resistant to viruses.

3. Explain *two* ways that GM foods can be used to help people in developing nations.

4. Explain why a person has most likely eaten a food with GM ingredients in it.

5. Describe the process of how scientists change the DNA of crops (plants) by using a gene gun.

6. (a) Describe the *two* main concerns that people have about GM foods. (b) For each concern, give *one* example of a report or event that caused this concern.

Going Further

With a partner, create a list of pros (benefits) and cons (drawbacks) of genetically modified foods. After you and your partner have written your list, pair up with another group to compare your ideas with what they have written. Add on to your list any additional items that the other group had written. Once you have your list, develop your own opinion about genetically modified foods in an essay.

Should People Make Designer Babies?

Imagine a world in which people could choose what their children would be like: they could decide the color of their hair and eyes, their height, and maybe even their athletic ability or intelligence level. Although this sounds like science fiction, some people believe this might be a reality in our future. You have already learned that gene therapy was developed to try to eliminate genetic diseases in people. Some of these diseases are fatal, so the use of gene therapy could potentially save a person's life. But what about altering a person's DNA for something that is not life-threatening, but is only a trait that parents would like to see in their future children? What about having the power to control whether a baby will be male or female? Is this an acceptable use of biotechnology? Read on and you can decide how you feel about the potential use of genetic engineering to change the traits of people.

When an unborn baby has had his or her genes artificially selected for by scientists, he or she is called a **designer baby**. This is a term that has been around for only a short time because the process is so new; it was only officially defined as recently as 2004. There are two processes making up the definition of a designer baby: the first is selecting an embryo that already has certain traits;

the second is directly changing the DNA of an embryo. An **embryo** is an organism in the early stages of development that is formed after a fertilized egg starts to divide (that is, make more cells). The type of embryo used in genetic engineering is usually a group of about eight to ten undifferentiated cells. (See Figure 5-17.)

Both of these processes use *in vitro fertilization* (IVF), meaning that the egg cell is fertilized by a sperm cell outside the mother's body (within a petri dish). The fertilized egg is grown into an embryo, which is then implanted into the mother's womb, where it can continue growing into a baby.

The first process, which was developed in the 1990s, is called **pre-implantation genetic diagnosis (PGD)**. This is the process by which scientists look for embryos that have certain desired traits and implant only those embryos into the womb of a woman. Scientists do this by fertilizing a few egg cells (by means of IVF) from the mother with sperm cells from the father. They wait until the embryos are about eight to ten cells in size and take out one cell from each embryo to see if it has the desired trait. They then implant those embryos into the mother. Usually scientists implant more than one embryo with the desired trait

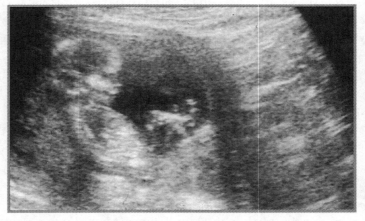

Figure 5-17. This ultrasonograph shows the outline of a developing fetus, that is, an embryo after the first three months of development. (*Note:* The fetus is facing the center of the image.) When an unborn baby has had his or her genes artificially selected for by scientists, he or she is called a designer baby.

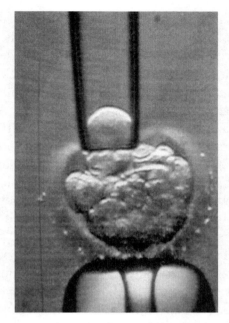

Figure 5-18. In the process of pre-implantation genetic diagnosis (PGD), shown above, scientists take one cell from each embryo to see if it has the desired trait before implanting those embryos into the mother.

in order to increase the chances that at least one embryo will successfully develop into a baby (not all embryos implanted grow to be babies). (See Figure 5-18.)

This PGD process was first developed to screen out embryos that had certain genetic diseases. Couples would use PGD if they knew that one or both of them were carriers for a genetic disease, thus eliminating the chance that their child would be born with that disease. The controversy began when people started to use PGD to select for a certain gender (male or female sex) of the embryo. Some people have argued that this could lead to an imbalance of the sexes in countries where one gender is preferred over another. In this type of procedure, if the scientists want to help the parents select embryos that have certain traits, such as a particular eye color, they are limited by the genes that the parents already have. That is, the scientists are not able to add new DNA to the embryos. So, for example, if neither parent has the genes for green eyes, none of the embryos will be able to have green eyes. (See Figure 5-19.)

The second way a designer baby could be created is by adding genes directly into an embryo. This type of genetic engineering has not yet been done in human embryos, but it has been done with mice. One example of this occurred 1999 when scientists at Princeton University created "Doogie" mice (named after an intelligent television character) with an extra NR2B gene, which is thought to have a positive effect on memory and intelligence. These designer Doogie mice appeared to learn more quickly and retain information longer than other mice that did not have the added NR2B gene. (See Figure 5-20 on page 164.)

There are many controversies regarding this kind of genetic engineering, especially as it applies to humans. One argument is that

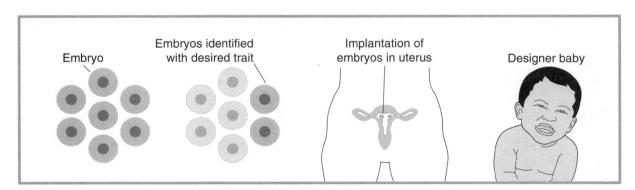

Figure 5-19. The diagram shows how PGD could be used to select for traits such as the preferred gender or eye color of a baby.

Figure 5-20. Scientists created the "Doogie" mouse by inserting an extra gene into its DNA, which was thought to enhance the mouse's memory and intelligence.

such a technique may have limited usefulness because many traits are controlled by more than one gene. Thus, being given an extra copy of just one gene will not necessarily guarantee a particular trait. Another argument is related to the "nature versus nurture" debate over how much certain traits, such as intelligence or athletic ability, are affected by the environment as well as by genes. In other words, by giving an embryo a gene that is linked to intelligence, a scientist does not necessarily make that embryo more intelligent.

Probably the biggest controversy over the development of designer babies is the concern that it will lead to some traits being considered better than others. For example, if this practice were to become common for human babies, people worry that parents may start choosing certain traits over others. At the same time—for better or worse—this is not a technique that everyone would have access to, since PGD can be very expensive. So this form of biotechnology might be available only to wealthy people. Another concern about using biotechnology to pick certain traits over others is that it reminds people of the ideas that were popular in the eugenics movement during the early part of the 1900s. People who followed **eugenics** thought certain physical and mental traits were more desirable than others. They believed that people with "good" traits should have more children than people with "bad" traits (for example, criminals). Thus, a serious issue that could arise over designer babies would be that of which traits are good, which traits are bad, and who has the right to make those decisions.

Some people would consider certain traits undesirable, but others would not. Generally, people are more comfortable with the idea of changing a person's DNA to eliminate a genetic disease rather than just to change a trait based on personal preference. Because of these controversies, PGD is heavily regulated in many countries and is allowed only for the prevention of genetic diseases in babies, not for creating designer babies. In the United States, however, PGD is legal and unregulated. Could designer babies be in our future? Only time will tell if such a practice becomes common in our lifetimes.

Vocabulary Check

For each of the following terms, give a complete definition.

1. Designer baby

2. Embryo

3. Pre-implantation genetic diagnosis (PGD)

4. Eugenics

Multiple Choice

For each question, choose the letter of the answer choice that best completes the sentence or answers the question.

1. The term "designer baby" officially entered our language in
   a. the early 1900s   b. 1994   c. 2004   d. 2009

2. In creating a designer baby, scientists would use an embryo made up of about _____ cells.
   a. one to two   b. eight to ten   c. 15 to 20   d. 50 to 60

3. PGD was first developed for couples who wanted to screen their embryos for a certain
   a. athletic ability   b. eye color   c. hair color   d. genetic disease

4. The Princeton "Doogie" mice were given a gene that appeared to have an effect on their
   a. fur color   b. weight   c. memory   d. eye color

5. The debate over the effect of genetics and environment on a person's development is called nature versus
   a. nurture   b. normal   c. nothing   d. neighbors

6. According to the ideas of eugenics, criminals would probably have _____ genes.
   a. too many   b. too few   c. good   d. bad

True or False

Read each statement and indicate whether it is true or false. If it is false, correct the underlined word(s) to make the statement true.

1. The process of creating designer babies using genetic engineering is relatively <u>new</u>.

   1. _____

2. Creating a designer baby requires a process called *in vivo* fertilization.

   2. _____

3. The technique of PGD began in the <u>1980s</u>.

   3. _____

4. PGD <u>does not change</u> the DNA of embryos.

   4. _____

5. Adding genes directly to an embryo to give it a different trait has been done <u>in people</u>.

   5. _____

6. PGD is a very <u>inexpensive</u> technique.

   6._____

Short Answer

Answer the following questions in one or two complete sentences.

1. What are the *two* ways scientists can create a designer baby?
2. Describe the steps that scientists use in the PGD technique.
3. How do some people think PGD might affect the balance of genders in certain countries?
4. What were the results of the experiments on the "Doogie" mice?
5. Describe at least *two* controversies about scientists creating designer babies.
6. Create a Venn diagram on another sheet of paper to compare and contrast eugenics and designer babies.

Going Further

Do you agree that genetic engineering should be used on people for *any* purposes? Would you use this process for your future children? Defend your position with *two* or *three* ideas and explain your reasoning.

Vocabulary Exercise: Splicing in Words About Gene Splicing

Directions: On a separate sheet of paper that your teacher has given to you, fill in the correct words from the "word bank" below. You may want to review your "Vocabulary Check" sections for Lessons 5.1 and 5.2 to help you remember the definitions for each term. *Note*: Some terms may be used more than once.

The following is a story about a scientist named Anna. Anna wants to create insulin from bacterial cells. Insulin is given to people with diabetes to regulate their blood sugar levels.

Anna wants to develop bacteria that produce insulin, so she needs to change the DNA of a bacterial cell. This is called (1) _____ _____.
Anna would start this process by taking the gene to make insulin from an organism that already makes it, such as a human. She would remove the gene for insulin from that human DNA by using a (2) _____ _____, which cuts DNA at very specific places. Then Anna would need to make room for the new gene in the circular DNA of the bacterial cell, which is called a (3) _____. She would cut open the DNA in the bacterial cell by using a (4) _____ _____ again. Then Anna would paste the gene for insulin into the DNA of the bacterium. The specific term for this process (of pasting in new genes) is called (5) _____ _____.
When Anna has done this, she has produced a new type of DNA called (6) _____ _____, which is a new combination of genetic material. This new DNA produces a special bacterial cell that is now a new type of organism called a (7) _____ _____, because it has DNA from a person as well as its own DNA. Anna will put her new bacterium into a (8) _____ to help it grow and multiply thousands of times. Now her thousands of genetically modified bacteria will be able to produce the insulin that is needed for people with diabetes.

Word Bank

restriction enzyme	**genetic engineering**
plasmid	**bioreactor**
gene splicing	**recombinant DNA**
transgenic organism	

Comparing Data on Genetically Modified Crops

When interpreting data from a table and putting it into a graph, a scientist must know what type of graph best suits the data. The three most common types of graphs are:

➤ Line graph—Shows one value that changes over time
➤ Pie graph—Shows parts of the whole (percentages)
➤ Bar graph—Compares amounts by how much or how many

The following tables have data about different aspects of genetically modified (GM) food. For each table, choose an appropriate graph (line, pie, or bar) to represent the data and draw it on a separate sheet of paper. Answer the questions that follow.

Table 1: Global GM Crop Plantings by Crop, 1996–2005			
Year	GM soybeans planted (in million hectares)	GM corn planted (in million hectares)	GM cotton planted (in million hectares)
1996	0.1	0.1	0.1
1997	5	3	1
1998	17	8	2
1999	24	10	3
2000	29	9	6
2001	35	10	7
2002	40	13	7
2003	43	16	8
2004	48	18	9
2005	54	19	10

Graph 1 Questions

1. Which graph is most appropriate for this set of data?
2. Why do you think this is the most appropriate graph?
3. From what you have learned in the section on GM foods, why do you think there was a dip in the amount of GM corn planted in 2000?
4. What is one piece of information you can conclude from looking at your graph?

Table 2: Amount of GM Crops Planted vs. Non-GM Crops Planted in 2005		
Crop	Amount of GM crops planted (in million hectares)	Amount of non-GM crops planted (in million hectares)
Soybeans	54	92
Corn	19	148
Cotton	10	36

Graph 2 Questions

1. Which graph is most appropriate for this set of data?
2. Why do you think this is the most appropriate graph?
3. (a) Which crop has the greatest difference between the non-GM variety planted as compared to the GM variety? (b) How many more hectares of the non-GM crop were planted?
4. What is one piece of information you can conclude from looking at your graph?

Table 3: Percent of GM Crops Grown Globally in 2005	
Country	Percent of all GM crops planted
United States	55
China	4
Canada	7
Brazil	10
Argentina	19
Others	5

Graph 3 Questions

1. Which graph is most appropriate for this set of data?
2. Why do you think this is the most appropriate graph?
3. Which country grows the highest percent of GM foods?
4. What is one piece of information you can conclude from looking at your graph?

You are working as a research scientist at an agricultural biotech company. Your team has to come up with a modified food crop through the use of genetic engineering. Your boss wants you to come up with a plan before you begin to work on the plant. Use what you have learned about genetically modified foods to develop your plan. On a separate sheet of paper, list the following information:

1. The food item you want to genetically engineer

2. The trait you want your new food plant to have

3. The organism you will take the desired gene from and why you will take it from this organism

4. The potential benefits of your food (for the consumer and/or farmer)

5. The potential drawbacks of your food (for the consumer and/or farmer)

6. The name of your new genetically modified food (crop)

7. The types of food/dishes your new food could be added to

> **On another sheet of paper, draw an advertisement for your new genetically modified food.**

Chapter 5 Review

Vocabulary Crossword

Directions: *Each clue below is a definition of one of the vocabulary words that you learned in this chapter. On a printout of this page provided by your teacher, write the word that matches each definition inside the numbered vertical or horizontal spaces. All the vocabulary words from Chapter 5 are used in this puzzle.*

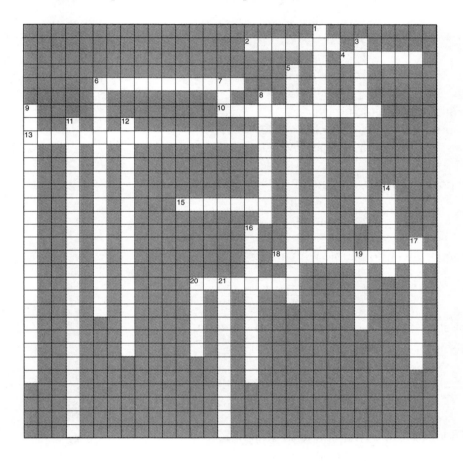

Across

2. A machine that shoots gene-coated pellets through cells of a plant in order to introduce a new gene to that plant

4. A transporter of DNA, which is usually a bacterium or a virus

6. A procedure that aims to fix the mutations in someone's DNA that cause a genetic disease or disorder

10. A child who has had his or her genes artificially selected for by scientists

13. When scientists use vectors to transport the correct gene directly into a person's body; a relatively simple way to give the organism the genes the scientist wants

15. A Latin term for "in the glass"

18. Chemicals that can kill insects

20. The idea that certain traits in people were more desirable than others and that the people with the "good" traits should be encouraged to have more children

Down

1. A protein that controls growth in the human body and is secreted by the pituitary gland

3. New DNA that is created from gene splicing

5. An organism that has DNA from another organism in its DNA

6. The process of changing an organism's DNA

7. A process in which scientists look for embryos that have certain traits and implant into the mother's womb only those that have the desired traits (use initials only)

8. A machine that provides the ideal temperature and nutrients to allow the bacteria to grow and multiply many times

9. Cells that have not yet become specialized

11. Plants and animals we eat that have had their DNA changed by scientists

12. Substances that will cut the DNA at very specific places

14. A loop of DNA in bacteria that is separate from the main bacterial DNA

16. A protein that is produced by the pancreas after a person has eaten and the body experiences high levels of glucose

17. Chemicals used to kill weeds that also can be harmful to crops

19. A Latin term for "in the living"

20. An organism in the early stages of development that is formed after a fertilized egg starts to divide

21. The process of cutting out a gene and putting it into a new strand of DNA

Multiple Choice

For each question, choose the letter of the answer choice that best completes the sentence or answers the question.

1. The purpose of genetic engineering is to _____ a trait of an organism.
   a. maintain   b. preserve   c. change   d. delete

2. Genes are added to an organism's DNA by using a
   a. vector   b. yeast cell   c. nucleus   d. scissors

3. A transgenic organism is one with a new
   a. DNA sequence   c. gene
   b. trait   d. all of the above

4. The first genetically engineered medicine was
   a. human growth hormone   c. penicillin
   b. human insulin   d. a type of vaccine

5. When people's bodies produce little to no insulin the disorder is called
   a. Type 1 diabetes   c. pancreatitis
   b. Type 2 diabetes   d. hepatitis

6. Human growth hormone is given to people who are
   a. tired   c. diabetic
   b. allergic to penicillin d. abnormally short

7. In gene therapy, scientists _____ a defective gene in a person.
   a. remove   b. rearrange   c. add   d. replace

8. There have been _____ problems with gene therapy experiments.
   a. no   b. some   c. a lot of   d. constant

9. Gene therapy is being looked into as a possible treatment for
   a. genetic diseases   c. mutations in DNA
   b. cancer   d. all of the above

10. The food that is most often genetically modified (GM) is
    a. tomatoes   b. corn   c. soy   d. canola

11. Genetically modified plants get new DNA by means of a(n)
    a. gene gun   b. bioreactor   c. insecticide   d. herbicide

12. In the United States, there are _____ laws requiring GM foods to be labeled.
    a. no   b. two   c. a few   d. multiple

13. Pre-implantation genetic diagnosis (PGD) was originally developed in the
   a. 1890s   b. early 1900s   c. 1980s   d. 1990s

14. During PGD, scientists are looking for certain _____ with specific traits.
   a. twins   b. parents   c. embryos   d. babies

15. In the United States, the practice of PGD is currently
   a. considered illegal   c. heavily regulated
   b. legal and unregulated   d. very inexpensive

True or False

Read each statement and indicate whether it is true or false. If it is false, correct the underlined word(s) to make the statement true.

1. Genetic engineering can be done only by <u>adding DNA</u>.   1. _____

2. To make genetically engineered human insulin, scientists use   2. _____
the bacteria called <u>*E. coli*</u>.

3. Insulin is given to people who have <u>heart problems</u>.   3. _____

4. Insulin is normally produced in the <u>pancreas</u>.   4. _____

5. The first gene therapy experiments were in <u>2000</u>.   5. _____

6. The first gene therapy was given to a girl with <u>cancer</u>.   6. _____

7. Currently, <u>anyone</u> can get gene therapy treatment.   7. _____

8. The first GM food was called the <u>*Flavr Savr*</u> tomato.   8. _____

9. It is estimated that <u>most foods</u> have GM food ingredients in them.   9. _____

10. Bt corn was developed to <u>be tolerant of herbicides</u>.   10. _____

11. PGD <u>cannot</u> be used to pick the gender of a baby.   11. _____

12. Doogie mice were given a gene that appeared to improve   12. _____
their <u>memory and intelligence</u>.

13. The potential to create designer babies is sometimes compared   13. _____
to the ideas of <u>eugenics</u>.

Short Answer

Answer the following questions in one or two complete sentences.

1. Describe the *four* steps involved in genetic engineering.
2. Explain the similarities and differences between genetic engineering and selective breeding.
3. What does insulin typically do in people's bodies after they eat a meal?
4. Describe how genetically engineered bacteria are made to produce insulin.
5. Compare and contrast genetically engineered insulin to insulin from pigs or cattle.
6. (a) Explain the difference between scientists doing gene therapy in vivo and in vitro. (b) Describe the advantages and disadvantages of both.
7. Describe the concerns people have about doing gene therapy on people.
8. Describe the differences between treating someone with gene therapy as compared to giving them genetically engineered medicine like insulin.
9. (a) List the *three* most common traits GM foods are made to have. (b) Give an example of a food with each type of trait.
10. Explain how a scientist could create a food that has been genetically modified to have a sweet taste.
11. Discuss why some people are concerned about the creation of GM foods.
12. Compare and contrast PGD with directly changing the DNA of an embryo.
13. Explain the controversies about creating a designer baby.

Going Further

1. Discuss how each of the following items is an example of biotechnology.

   Genetically modified bacteria
   Gene therapy
   Genetically modified foods
   Designer babies

2. With a partner, create a collage of images that represents the different facets of genetic engineering. Your collage can include images or words from magazines, newspapers, or the Internet. Attach an explanation to your collage in which you describe why you chose specific images and/or words (pick *ten* images or words to explain). You will be graded according to the rubric provided by your teacher.

3. (a) Your teacher will put up four signs around the classroom: "Strongly disagree," "Disagree," "Agree," and "Strongly agree." For each of the four types of genetic engineering you have learned about in this chapter (genetically engineered bacteria, gene therapy, genetically modified food, and designer babies), decide how you feel about them.

   (b) Your teacher will then call out one topic at a time.

   (c) Go to the sign that best describes how you feel about that topic. Be prepared to explain why you feel that way.

   (d) Your teacher will repeat this process for each of the four topics.

CHAPTER

6

Stem Cells
and Cloning

Essential Question:
Should scientists
continue doing
research on cloning
and stem cells?

Contents

What Is So Important About Stem Cells?

Imagine if doctors could cure someone who had diabetes, Alzheimer's disease, or heart disease; or if someone who had become paralyzed from damage to their spinal cord could learn to walk again. While cures for these conditions do not yet exist, scientists hope that someday they will, with the help of research done on *stem cells*. Before you learn more about stem cells and why scientists use them for medical research, we will review information on how an organism develops.

In sexual reproduction, a new organism forms when an egg cell is fertilized by a sperm cell. The fertilized egg begins to divide, which creates an embryo. At first, all the cells in an embryo are the same; that is, none of the cells have a specific job to do, so they are still **unspecialized cells**. However, as the embryo develops, its cells change and then have specific jobs to do; that is, they become **specialized cells**. As the cells start to change, or *differentiate*, into specialized cells, they become any of over 200 different cell types in the human body. These include such types as muscle, fat, bone, blood, and nerve cells. Once a cell has become specialized, it cannot turn into any other type of cell. Those unspecialized cells that make up the embryo in its early stages of development are called **stem cells**, and they have two unique qualities: They can produce copies of themselves indefinitely and they can change into other types of cells. (See Figure 6-1.)

The unspecialized cells in an embryo that differentiate into most cell types of an organism are called **embryonic stem cells**. When an embryo is fertilized *in vivo* (inside a female), the stem cells that make up an embryo quickly start to become specialized, forming the different types of cells needed to create an organism. Once an organism has fully developed (and is born), it does not have any more embryonic stem cells. Scientists first isolated embryonic stem cells from mice in 1981; but it was only relatively recently, in 1998, that scientists were able to isolate embryonic stem cells from people. Because of this, there is still a lot that scientists have to learn about how embryonic stem cells could be used to treat human diseases.

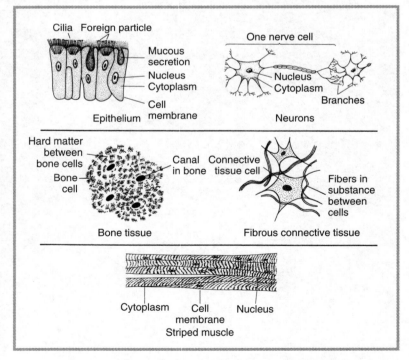

Figure 6-1. More than 200 different types of cells make up the human body. Stem cells in embryos have the ability to turn into any other type of cell.

What makes embryonic stem cells so intriguing to scientists is that they have the ability to turn into any type of cell; and scientists would like to be able to harness that potential for three reasons. The first reason is to use stem cells to study diseases. Researchers would do this by studying stem cells known to have a genetic mutation that will result in their developing a genetic disease. Scientists would like to study how these cells develop, which might result in finding ways to prevent these diseases. The second use is to test the safety and effectiveness of new drugs on cells created from embryonic stem cells. The third potential use of stem cells is to produce different types of cells that doctors could give to people who have damaged tissues and organs (which are made up of cells).

One possibility scientists are investigating is to see if embryonic stem cells can be turned into the islet cells of the pancreas (which produce insulin) to see if they can be given to people with diabetes (who do not produce enough insulin). Other areas of research include trying to learn if embryonic stem cells can be used to grow new heart cells to repair damaged heart tissue after a person has suffered a heart attack. Scientists are also conducting research to see if stem cells can be used to grow new nerve cells to treat Parkinson's disease and spinal cord injuries. So far, such experiments have been conducted on animals that have these conditions and they have appeared to be successful at treating these diseases. However, using embryonic stem cells to treat disease has only just started to be attempted in people.

Once scientists have an embryo, they allow it to grow for about five days into a

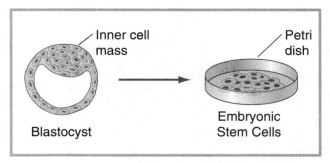

Figure 6-2. **Scientists take embryonic stem cells from the inner cell mass of blastocysts and maintain them in a petri dish before turning them into other cell types.**

blastocyst, which is the term for a mammal's embryo in the early stages of development (a ball of 150 cells). Scientists take the embryonic stem cells from inside the blastocyst, that is, from its *inner cell mass. Note:* After the embryonic stem cells are taken out of the blastocyst, it cannot develop any further. How do scientists get embryos for stem cell research? Scientists get embryos that are left over from in vitro fertilization (IVF) treatments. These IVF treatments are usually for couples who have had difficulty conceiving a baby. Scientists usually fertilize multiple egg cells because it often takes many attempts for an implanted embryo to develop into a baby. Hence, there are more embryos created than are needed; so the embryos that are not needed are kept frozen or are discarded. There are currently about 400,000 frozen embryos in the United States; of those, 2.8 percent have been donated for scientific research. (See Figure 6-2.)

When the embryonic stem cells are taken for research, they are maintained in petri dishes. The challenge for scientists is to figure out what type of signal to give the cells in order to turn them into each type of cell. Certain cellular signals will turn stem cells into heart cells and others will turn them into nerve cells. So far, scientists have had success in creating a variety of cells from embryonic stem cells, including white blood cells, heart cells, nerve cells, skeletal muscle cells, lung cells, islet (pancreatic) cells, and retinal cells. (See Figure 6-3 on page 178.)

Aside from embryonic stem cells, there are two other types of stem cells. One of these types is called *adult stem cells.* **Adult stem cells** are unspecialized cells that are found in certain parts of an organism's body

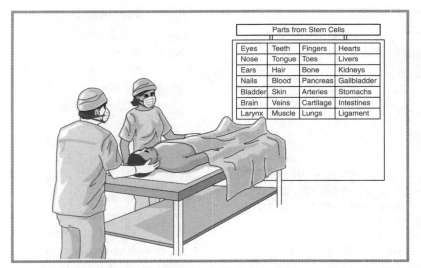

Parts from Stem Cells			
Eyes	Teeth	Fingers	Hearts
Nose	Tongue	Toes	Livers
Ears	Hair	Bone	Kidneys
Nails	Blood	Pancreas	Gallbladder
Bladder	Skin	Arteries	Stomachs
Brain	Veins	Cartilage	Intestines
Larynx	Muscle	Lungs	Ligament

Figure 6-3. Scientists have successfully created a variety of cell types from embryonic stem cells. One hope is that, someday, this research could lead to the production of spare human parts for medical operations.

and which are used to maintain and repair the tissue in which they are found. It appears that, unlike embryonic stem cells, adult stem cells are more limited in the types of cells that they can become. For example, adult stem cells in the liver appear to be able to turn only into other liver cells. However, scientists are conducting much research to learn if it is possible for adult stem cells to turn into a wider variety of cell types. Also, unlike embryonic stem cells, adult stem cells are not collected from a developing embryo. They are only gathered from existing tissue. Another difference is that adult stem cells have been used many times in stem cell experiments in people, whereas embryonic stem cells are just beginning to be approved for human stem cell experiments.

Adult stem cells have not been found in all parts of the body, but so far scientists have located them in the brain, bone marrow, skin, liver, skeletal muscle, blood vessels, and even amniotic fluid (fluid that surrounds a developing embryo). The stem cells in bone marrow are used to grow new blood cells for patients who get a bone marrow transplant. Adult stem cells have also been located in tissue from a fetus (the stage of development after embryo but before birth), as well as in umbilical cord blood. Adult stem cells from these sources have been used in experiments on many different disorders and seem to be more versatile than other types of adult stem cells.

The latest development in stem cell research has been carried out on yet a different kind of cell. In 2007, a type of stem cell was produced from human cells that are similar to embryonic stem cells. These cells, called **induced pluripotent stem cells**, are thought to have the ability to turn into many different cell types. The word *pluripotent* can be broken down into two parts—*pluri* is Latin for "many" and *potent* means "to be able" (or "ability"). Put together, it means that if a cell is pluripotent it has the ability to turn into many of the different cell types that make up an organism. Induced pluripotent stem cells are created by "reprogramming" cells in the body by turning on specific genes that allow the cells to be flexible. So far, the most common source for creating these stem cells has been adult skin cells. Recently, researchers have also used immune cells from human blood to create induced pluripotent stem cells. Scientists are interested in doing research on this type of stem cell because it lets them have cells that can turn into many cell types without having to use embryonic cells. This field is still quite new and more research needs to be done in this area.

While the use of stem cells appears to open many doors to the possible treatment of diseases, it also is highly controversial. These controversies and current legislation will be discussed later in this chapter.

Lesson 6.1 Review

Vocabulary Check

For each of the following terms, give a complete definition.

1. Unspecialized cells

2. Specialized cells

3. Stem cells

4. Embryonic stem cells

5. Blastocyst

6. Adult stem cells

7. Induced pluripotent stem cells

Multiple Choice

For each question, choose the letter of the answer choice that best completes the sentence or answers the question.

1. In the beginning stage of development, all cells of an embryo are
   a. unspecialized   b. specialized   c. nerve cells   d. blood cells

2. There are about _____ types of cells in the human body.
   a. 50   b. 150   c. 200   d. 300

3. Scientists are hoping to use stem cells to treat
   a. damaged heart tissue   c. paralysis
   b. Parkinson's disease   d. all of the above

4. Once embryonic stem cells are taken out of it, a blastocyst can _____ develop further.
   a. rarely   b. sometimes   c. always   d. not

5. Scientists first isolated human embryonic stem cells in the year
   a. 1981   b. 1989   c. 1998   d. 2007

6. The stem cells in bone marrow are used in patients to grow new
   a. blood cells   b. nerve cells   c. muscle cells   d. bones

True or False

Read each statement and indicate whether it is true or false. If it is false, correct the underlined word(s) to make the statement true.

1. Once a cell has become specialized, it <u>can become</u> other types of cells.

1._____

2. A two-year-old child has <u>some</u> embryonic stem cells.

2._____

3. So far, experiments using embryonic stem cells on mice have been shown to be <u>successful</u>.

3._____

4. Embryonic stem cells are found in the <u>outer</u> part of the blastocyst.

4._____

5. Adult stem cells have been found <u>in certain parts</u> of the body.

5._____

6. Adult stem cells <u>can</u> turn into any cell of the body.

6._____

Short Answer

Answer the following questions in one or two complete sentences.

1. (a) Explain the difference between an unspecialized cell and a specialized cell.
   (b) Give *one* example of each.
2. Describe *three* reasons why scientists are interested in doing stem cell research.
3. From where do scientists get the embryos needed for stem cell research?
4. List the types of cells that scientists have created from embryonic stem cells.
5. Once scientists have an embryonic stem cell, what is the challenge they face?
6. On a separate sheet of paper, copy and complete this Venn diagram in which you will compare and contrast embryonic stem cells and adult stem cells.

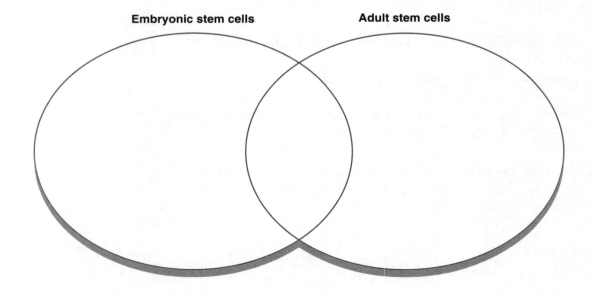

Embryonic stem cells   Adult stem cells

7. How do stem cells from fetal tissue and umbilical cord blood differ from other types of adult stem cells?
8. (a) How do scientists create induced pluripotent cells? (b) Why are scientists interested in researching this type of stem cell?

Going Further

1. Math skills: If 2.8 percent of the 400,000 frozen embryos in the Unites States are donated for stem cell research, how many embryos are donated?

2. Draw a picture to represent several of the vocabulary words. Write each vocabulary term below its picture. You may organize your words and pictures any way you would like.

How Do Scientists Carry Out Cloning?

When most people hear the term *cloning*, what probably comes to mind is a scene of "mad scientists" creating an exact copy of a person. They might envision a giant machine that a person steps into, and then multiple copies of that person coming out. However, this is not how cloning is done (and it is not even done on humans). Just as people may have misconceptions about genetic engineering, many have the wrong idea about how cloning is done and even why scientists are using this form of biotechnology. (See Figure 6-4.)

When you hear the word *clone*, you might think of a copy of something. This is a common definition. When scientists use the term **clone** they are referring to an organism (or part of an organism) that is the exact genetic match of another organism. Contrary to the idea that a clone is something that belongs in a science fiction movie, there are clones among us every day. Identical twins are, in fact, clones of each other because they are an

exact genetic match. Such twins are examples of how clones can occur naturally. (Refer to Figure 3-9a on page 71.)

So how do scientists create a clone? The first thing that scientists need to produce a clone is a somatic cell. A **somatic cell** is any cell in an organism other than a sperm cell or egg cell. In other words, it is a body cell, such as a skin, liver, or heart cell, not a reproductive cell. All somatic cells in an organism have the same DNA; and this DNA is a complete set of instructions for making the organism.

The first step in cloning is for the scientists to take a somatic cell from a donor organism that they want to clone, and **enucleate** (remove the nucleus from) the cell. They keep the nucleus but discard the rest of the cell. The second step is to take an egg cell from a female of the same species, enucleate that cell, but keep the empty egg cell. They remove the nucleus because they don't want any genetic material from this organism left over in the egg cell. The third step is to insert the nucleus from the first organism into the enucleated egg cell. Next, they wait several hours for the egg cell to become "reprogrammed" with the new nucleus in it. Certain chemicals are added to the egg cell to encourage it to divide and eventually form an embryo. This process of transferring the nucleus from a somatic cell (of the organism to be cloned) into an enucleated egg cell is called **somatic cell nuclear transfer**. (See Figure 6-5.)

The final step of somatic cell nuclear transfer will depend on what the scientist would like to create. When scientists use cloning only to produce certain cells or tissues of an organism, it is called **therapeutic cloning**. When scientists clone a whole individual, it is called **reproductive cloning**. Therapeutic cloning involves taking the cloned embryo,

Figure 6-4. Many people have the wrong idea about how cloning is done; this is how some people mistakenly think of the process.

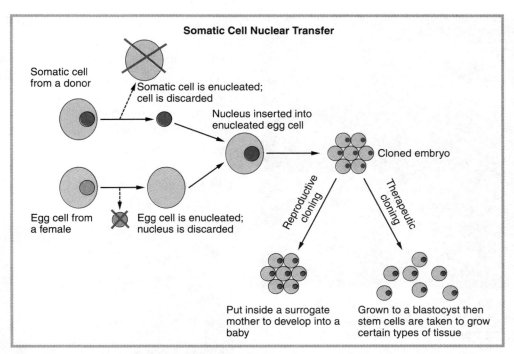

Somatic Cell Nuclear Transfer

Somatic cell from a donor

Somatic cell is enucleated; cell is discarded

Nucleus inserted into enucleated egg cell

Cloned embryo

Egg cell from a female

Egg cell is enucleated; nucleus is discarded

Reproductive cloning

Therapeutic cloning

Put inside a surrogate mother to develop into a baby

Grown to a blastocyst then stem cells are taken to grow certain types of tissue

Figure 6-5. **Somatic cell nuclear transfer: The process of transferring the nucleus from a somatic cell into an enucleated egg cell.**

growing it into a blastocyst and then removing the stem cells from inside the blastocyst. These cells are given specific signals to make them grow into different types of cells that will be a genetic match to the donor of the somatic cell. Scientists want to use this type of cloning to create stem cells that could be used to grow new cells and tissue for people with a diseased organ. As discussed in the last section, they could make islet cells for people with diabetes, or new heart tissue for people with a damaged heart. Making tissue that is a genetic match to a patient would mean that there would be no possibility of rejection, which occurs when the immune system does not accept new tissue or a new organ. To date, the use of somatic cell nuclear transfer to create human embryonic stem cells is only being carried out in a few research laboratories.

With reproductive cloning, scientists would follow the same procedure as therapeutic cloning, except instead of growing the embryo into a blastocyst to use its stem cells, they would take the embryo and implant it into another female animal's womb. This fe-

male is called the *surrogate* mother, because she is not the real mother of the embryo (that is, she did not contribute any genetic material), but she will be pregnant with it and then deliver the baby. The first time cloning was used to produce an animal from an adult somatic cell was in 1996. A cloned sheep named Dolly was produced at the Roslin Institute in Scotland. Since then, many other mammals have been cloned, such as dogs, cats, rabbits, mice, goats, pigs, cows, and monkeys, Before Dolly the sheep, scientists had made clones of animals, but they had cloned only cells from embryos (essentially creating identical twins), not from an adult animal. (See Figures 6-6a and b on page 184.)

Why would people want to use reproductive cloning to produce a whole animal? One possible use of reproductive cloning is to clone endangered species or possibly even extinct animals. Animals that are on the verge of becoming extinct could get a population boost if some cloned animals were produced. Also, for animals that recently went extinct, if scientists still have tissue samples (with an

Figure 6-6a. In 1996, in Scotland, a sheep named Dolly was the first animal produced by cloning from an adult somatic cell.

intact nucleus and undamaged DNA), they might be able to clone them if they have a closely related or similar species to use for the egg cell and as the surrogate mother. This concept was made famous in the science-fiction novel and movie *Jurassic Park*, in which scientists on a remote island cloned dinosaur DNA and used reproductive cloning to produce numerous dinosaur species.

As interesting as it might seem to want to clone long-extinct dinosaur species, there are two major problems in trying to do so. The first is that it would most likely be impossible to find an intact nucleus with undamaged DNA from over 65 million years ago; cells (and the DNA in them) degrade after an organism dies. The second problem would be finding a species to use for the egg cell and as the surrogate mother. Both animals would need to be very closely related, if not the same species; and that would be a problem since there are no dinosaurs or close relatives alive today. (See Figure 6-7.)

Figure 6-7. Although the movie *Jurassic Park* made it seem possible, it is, in fact, impossible for scientists to clone any dinosaur species.

Although researchers and private companies have performed reproductive cloning on animals, no serious scientists have expressed the desire to clone an entire human. They are more interested in performing therapeutic cloning for medical purposes. However, the possibility of cloning an entire human being has sparked much debate. (Note that it is illegal to clone a human being; this will be discussed further in the next section.) Keep in mind that if a person were cloned, he or she would be essentially an identical twin of the person from whom he or she were cloned, but they

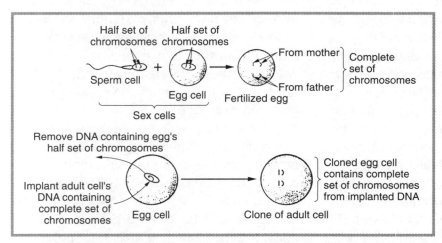

Figure 6-6b. A comparison of the natural fertilization process and the cloning process.

would be younger than the original person. For example, if scientists were to clone a 13-year-old boy, they would take a somatic cell from him to use his DNA and then put it into an enucleated egg cell. The resulting embryo would then be implanted into the womb of a surrogate mother. When the clone is born almost a year later, he would be nearly 14 years younger than the boy from whom he was cloned. The scientists would have created an identical, but much younger, twin brother of the boy.

As you might imagine, the process of using stem cells and cloning has created much controversy. Some scientists argue that there would be many benefits from using these processes to help treat human diseases. Other people argue that carrying out these techniques is highly unethical. The next section discusses viewpoints from both sides, as well as discussing the current laws regarding both stem cells and cloning.

Lesson 6.2 Review

Vocabulary Check

For each of the following terms, give a complete definition.

1. Clone

2. Somatic cell

3. Enucleate

4. Somatic cell nuclear transfer

5. Therapeutic cloning

6. Reproductive cloning

Multiple Choice

For each question, choose the letter of the answer choice that best completes the sentence or answers the question.

1. Twins, like clones, have _____ of the same DNA.
   a. none   b. some   c. most   d. all

2. Which one of the following is a type of somatic cell?
   a. sperm cell   b. egg cell   c. skin cell   d. all of these

3. Therapeutic cloning is used to create
   a. stem cells   b. a person   c. animals   d. sperm cells

4. Reproductive cloning involves using _____ organisms.
   a. one   b. two   c. three   d. four

5. Scientists created the first cloned animal from an adult cell in
   a. 1995   b. 1996   c. 1997   d. 1998

6. The first cloned mammal made from an adult cell was a
   a. sheep   b. pig   c. dog   d. cow

True or False

Read each statement and indicate whether it is true or false. If it is false, correct the underlined word(s) to make the statement true.

1. Scientists <u>create clones</u> by putting people in a cloning machine.   1._____

2. <u>Identical twins</u> are examples of naturally occurring clones.   2._____

3. <u>Some</u> somatic cells in an organism have the same DNA.   3._____

4. If a cell has been enucleated, it has had a nucleus <u>added to it</u>.   4._____

5. Cloning a whole animal (such as a cat or dog) <u>has been done</u>.   5._____

6. Cloning a whole human being <u>has been done</u>.   6._____

Short Answer

Answer the following questions in one or two complete sentences.

1. Describe, in several steps, how scientists create a cloned embryo.
2. Why do scientists remove the nucleus from an egg cell in somatic cell nuclear transfer?
3. Identify *one* difference and *one* similarity between therapeutic and reproductive cloning.
4. Explain the advantage of using therapeutic cloning to create cells and tissues that are a genetic match to a patient.
5. Why is a surrogate mother not the real (biological) mother of a cloned animal?
6. If you were cloned, what would the age of your clone be? Explain why your clone would be this age.

Going Further

1. Read the passage below and then answer the following: (a) What will be the color of the cloned cat? (b) Explain why it will be this color.

> Scientists would like to make a clone of a white cat. They take a somatic cell from that cat, and transfer the nucleus into an enucleated egg cell from a black cat. The embryo that is formed is then placed into a surrogate mother, who is a brown cat.

2. When creating a clone, scientists take the nucleus from a somatic cell of an organism (any cell other than a reproductive cell; that is, *not* an egg cell or sperm cell). Why do you think they must use the DNA in the nucleus of a somatic cell to make a clone rather than a nucleus from a reproductive cell?

Lesson 6.3 What Are the Ethical Issues and Laws?

As excited as many researchers and patients may be over the advances made in stem cell and therapeutic cloning research, there are also some people who feel uneasy with this type of biotechnology. The issue of whether or not scientists should be manipulating embryos for possible use in the treatment of disease raises many ethical issues. An **ethical issue** involves determining if something is morally right or wrong. With ethical issues, there is not always a clear right or wrong answer; there can be more than one viewpoint on the issue.

Figure 6-8. The late actor Christopher Reeve, who was paralyzed after an accident, spoke out in favor of stem cell research to try to find a cure for people with paralysis.

Cloning and stem cell research are areas of scientific research that can cause people to feel very strongly about the ethics involved. The debate centers on the source of the stem cells; that is, the use of leftover embryos from IVF clinics and the use of therapeutic cloning to create embryos (for stem cells).

People who support stem cell research and therapeutic cloning believe that the cells and tissues generated could lead to new treatments for people who have diabetes, paralysis, Parkinson's disease, and other conditions. They argue that the possible medical benefits of doing embryonic stem cell research justify the use of the embryos. However, people who are against stem cell research believe that it is wrong to destroy an embryo; and that it is the equivalent of destroying a human life. They argue that life begins at the moment an egg cell is fertilized. On the other hand, supporters of stem cell research and therapeutic cloning would counter that the embryos used for stem cell research (which are left over after fertility treatments) would have been discarded or kept frozen and so would not have developed into a human, unless the embryo were implanted into a woman. Various religious groups have also taken different stands on the issue. (See Figure 6-8.)

People are very passionate on both sides of this debate. Generally, research involving adult stem cells (including those from amniotic fluid or an umbilical cord) is not debated or disputed in the way that the use of embryonic stem cells is, because these cells are isolated without using an embryo. A possible compromise for these two sides of the stem cell debate came in 2006, when a biotechnology company called Advanced Cell Technology claimed to have developed a method of getting embryonic stem cells from an embryo by removing just one cell from an eight-to-ten-celled embryo, which would still leave the embryo with the ability to develop into a baby (if implanted into a female). This research is still very new and much more work needs to be done to develop the procedure.

Figure 6-9. There is usually a lot of genetic variation within a species, which helps it survive. So there is concern that a population of cloned organisms would be susceptible to being wiped out by a new infection. Cheetahs, much like clones, are all nearly genetically identical, thus making this endangered species very vulnerable to extinction.

members, because of their genetic makeup, will be better able to fight off infection than others. The concern is that a population of cloned plants or animals could be wiped out by a new infection if they all have the gene that makes them susceptible to it. (See Figure 6-9.)

So far, the discussion has focused on the debate about the use of embryonic stem cells (or therapeutic cloning to get stem cells). There is also debate about the reproductive cloning of animals and the possibility that this may lead the way to reproductive cloning of people. It has been noted that cloned animals have more health problems than non-cloned animals of the same species, and they also tend to die at an earlier-than-normal age. Dolly, for example, lived to be only six years old (sheep can typically live twice that long) and she had health problems such as arthritis and lung disease. Some people argue that it is not ethical to clone animals, knowing that they will face these health problems. They also argue that it would be unethical to clone a person, knowing that they too might have more health problems and die at an earlier age.

Another argument that some people state against the use of reproductive cloning on plants and animals is that it could result in a loss of biodiversity. **Biodiversity** is the variety of traits within and between species, and the variety of species within ecosystems. Typically, there is a lot of genetic variation among plants and animals. So, if harmful bacteria or viruses attack a population, some

Another argument that people have against using reproductive cloning on animals or on people is that the cloned organism might not be exactly like the animal or person from which they were cloned. There are a few companies that can clone a beloved family pet (cat or dog) that has passed away. However, there is no guarantee that the cloned pet will have the same behavior as the original animal because the cloned animal will have different experiences that could affect it. Also, if scientists were permitted to clone a famous athlete, people might expect the cloned person to have the same skills in a particular sport as the original person. Suppose the cloned person had neither the skill nor the desire to play that sport. Would such people feel great pressure to do something they do not want to do? (See Figure 6-10 on page 190.)

When thinking about this, remember the debate about nature vs. nurture that was discussed in an earlier chapter. The debate questioned whether a person was more influenced by *nature* (their DNA) or *nurture* (their environment and the way in which they were raised). It could be said that people's behavior, including their likes and dislikes, are definitely influenced by their genes, but people are also

Figure 6-10. If scientists were permitted to clone an athlete, people might expect the clones to have the same skills in the particular sport as the original person, but there is no guarantee that this would really happen.

affected by their environment. Just like identical twins, a clone and the person from whom he was cloned would have the same genes but would have had different experiences in life, thus leading to differences in behavior.

With all these controversies about the use of cloning and stem cells, you might suppose that there are many laws regulating these procedures. However, laws affecting cloning and stem cell research vary from state to state and from country to country; they can also change depending on who is in power. There are no federal laws that control cloning in the United States; it is up to each state to pass its own laws about use of this technology. Only 15 states have laws that regulate reproductive or therapeutic cloning (all other states have no laws for these procedures). As you can see from the table to the right, there are differences between the state laws on cloning. The penalties for breaking these laws range from fines ($50,000 to $1 million) to prison time (up to ten years in some states).

A variety of national laws are in place to regulate stem cell research. Some countries have strict laws regarding if or how scientists can perform embryonic stem cell research. Of the countries that do allow embryonic stem cell research, the laws mostly restrict scientists to using embryos that were already in existence and were going to be discarded from

Human Cloning Legislation in the United States		
State	Ban on reproductive cloning?	Ban on therapeutic cloning?
Arizona	No public $	No public $
Arkansas	Yes	Yes
California	Yes	No
Connecticut	Yes	No
Indiana	Yes	No
Iowa	Yes	Yes
Maryland	Yes	No
Massachusetts	Yes	No
Michigan	Yes	Yes
Missouri	No state $	No
New Jersey	Yes	No
North Dakota	Yes	Yes
Rhode Island	Yes	No
South Dakota	Yes	Yes
Virginia	Yes	Unclear

IVF clinics. In the United States, in 2001, President G. W. Bush signed a law that limited federal funding for stem cell research to work on only those cell lines that had been created prior to the law being signed. Although it did not ban all embryonic stem cell research, the law significantly limited the research that could be done. As a result, many scientists working on stem cells had to rely on funding from private companies, since research is usually very expensive. On March 9, 2009, President Obama signed into effect an order that reversed President Bush's legislation, making it possible for scientists to receive federal funds to carry out research on many new stem cell lines. However, in August 2010, a federal judge blocked President Obama's ruling, saying it violated a ban on the use of federal money for embryonic stem cell research. But a court decision in September temporarily allowed the funding to continue until the case is finally settled. (See Figure 6-11.)

Figure 6-11. **In March 2009, President Obama signed into effect a law that made it possible for scientists to receive federal funds to carry out stem cell research.**

The future of stem cell research and cloning remains unclear, as different countries develop their laws governing such research and as the public debates these controversial topics. What is clear, however, is that these developments in biotechnology have forever changed the way we think about scientists' ability to affect the world. Finally, just as with the stem cell and cloning issues, people must be advocates for a balance between scientific knowledge, technological ability, and their combined effects on society.

Vocabulary Check

For each of the following terms, give a complete definition.

1. Ethical issue

2. Biodiversity

Multiple Choice

For each question, choose the letter of the answer choice that best completes the sentence or answers the question.

1. An ethical issue involves determining if something is _____ right or wrong.
   a. morally   b. socially   c. technically   d. mentally

2. Embryos used in stem cell research come from
   a. adult stem cells   b. IVF clinics   c. liver cells   d. nerve cells

3. Cloned animals typically have _____ health problems compared to non-cloned animals of the same species.
   a. no   b. few   c. some   d. more

4. The nature *vs.* nurture debate questions the extent to which _____ can affect a person.
   a. DNA   b. genes   c. environment   d. all of these

5. Currently, _____ states have laws that regulate human cloning.
   a. all 50   b. 35   c. 15   d. 8

6. Penalties for breaking cloning laws may include
   a. a $50,000 fine   c. prison time
   b. a $1,000,000 fine   d. all of the above

True or False

Read each statement and indicate whether it is true or false. If it is false, correct the underlined word(s) to make the statement true.

1. Ethical issues <u>always</u> have a clear right or wrong answer.   1._____

2. Different religious groups have <u>the same</u> views on stem cell research.   2._____

3. Generally, adult stem cell research is <u>not debated</u> as much as embryonic stem cell research.

3._____

4. Cloned animals tend to live <u>longer lives</u> than non-cloned animals of the same species.

4._____

5. Cloned animals <u>might not</u> have the same behavior as the animal from which they were cloned.

5._____

6. There are <u>no federal laws</u> to control cloning in the United States.

6._____

7. Scientific research is usually <u>very inexpensive</u> to fund.

7._____

Short Answer

Answer the following questions in one or two complete sentences.

1. Describe *one* argument people have in support of embryonic stem cell research.
2. Describe *one* argument people can make against embryonic stem cell research.
3. Explain the concern about cloned animals and possible infections.
4. Speculate if a person who was cloned from one of your cells would have the same personality as you. Justify your answer.
5. What, if any, laws about cloning are there in your state?
6. How was legislation about embryonic stem cell research changed by President Obama?

Going Further

1. With a partner, create *two* lists of pros and cons, one about cloning (therapeutic and reproductive) and one about embryonic stem cells. Once all groups have prepared their lists, write a list on the board of the pros and cons.

2. Imagine you are a U.S. Senator and are trying to establish federal laws regarding cloning and stem cells. With a partner or in a group of three, create a proposal for the laws that your constituents would like to see about cloning and stem cells. In your proposal, include:

- Specific definition of what is allowed and what is not allowed. Include specific definitions of each procedure so that scientists are clear about what they can and cannot do
- Appropriate punishment for the things that are not allowed if people are caught breaking the laws
- How scientists will be monitored to check that they are following the laws

Graphing Skills

Print This

What do others think about cloning and stem cells?

Viewpoints on the use of therapeutic cloning and stem cells can vary widely. Refer to the following Web site to research the laws that certain countries have about these fields of biotechnology.

Global laws on cloning and stem cells: **http://pewforum.org/docs/?DocID=318**

After your research, complete the following activities:

1. Summarize the laws for each country listed. Complete this chart (on a separate sheet of paper) by writing in each country listed on the Web site and checking off each category that describes that country's laws regarding reproductive cloning, therapeutic cloning, and stem cell research.

Global laws about cloning and stem cell research			
Country	Allows reproductive cloning (in humans)?	Allows therapeutic cloning (in humans)?	Allows for stem cell research?
South Africa			
China			
India			
Japan			
Singapore			
South Korea			
Belgium			

Country	Allows reproductive cloning (in humans)?	Allows therapeutic cloning (in humans)?	Allows for stem cell research?
France			
Germany			
Italy			
Spain			
Sweden			
United Kingdom			
Israel			
South Arabia			
Canada			
Mexico			
Brazil			

Put a * next to the countries that limit stem cell research to only using leftover embryos from IVF clinics.

Put a ** next to the countries that allow stem cell research only on embryonic stem cells that were imported from other countries.

2. Create a graph showing the number of countries that allow reproductive cloning, therapeutic cloning, and/or stem cell research. Determine what type of graph would be most appropriate for showing this information.

3. From looking at the data in your table and on your graph, what conclusion(s) can you draw about international laws regarding cloning and stem cell research?

Student Activity with Graphing Skills

Print This

stem cells and cloning survey

Complete this survey on stem cells and cloning by evaluating how you feel about these topics. Some demographic (personal background) information will also be collected. The results will be compared to those of your classmates in order to determine how the class feels about stem cells and cloning and also to see if the survey shows any trends about who supports or does not support such research.

Part 1 (a): Your views on stem cells and cloning

Rate how you feel about each of the statements below on a scale of 1 to 5; that is, from 1 (Strongly disagree) to 5 (Strongly agree).

	5 Strongly agree	4 Agree	3 Unsure	2 Disagree	1 Strongly disagree
1. Using reproductive cloning to clone a person's pet is okay.					
2. Using reproductive cloning to clone endangered or extinct species is okay.					
3. Using reproductive cloning to clone people is okay.					
4. Using therapeutic cloning to clone an embryo in order to get embryonic stem cells to give to people with damaged tissue, organs, or a certain disease is okay.					

	5 Strongly agree	4 Agree	3 Unsure	2 Disagree	1 Strongly disagree
5. Using therapeutic cloning to clone cells in order to study how diseased cells grow is okay.					
6. Using adult stem cells to give to people with damaged tissue, organs, or a certain disease is okay.					
7. Using embryonic stem cells from leftover embryos at IVF clinics in order to give to people with damaged tissue, organs, or a certain disease is okay.					
8. The government should give money to scientists for embryonic stem cell research.					
9. The government should have laws regulating cloning and stem cells.					

Part 1 (b): Your demographic information

Answer the following background information questions about yourself.

What is your gender? (male or female) _____

Does your family have a pet? _____

Do you know anyone who has a medical issue that is the result of a damaged organ, tissue, or cells (e.g., diabetes, paralysis, Parkinson's disease, stroke, heart attack, and so on) or do you have a medical issue yourself? _____

Data from Cloning and Stem Cell Survey

Sheet A

Part 2 (a): Data collection

Directions: Add up the total **number** of students for each statement that belong in each category (i.e., Strongly agree, Agree, etc.) and write each number in its respective category.

Statement	Number of students who feel this way				
	Strongly agree	Agree	Unsure	Disagree	Strongly disagree
1. Using reproductive cloning to clone a person's pet is okay.					
2. Using reproductive cloning to clone endangered or extinct species is okay.					
3. Using reproductive cloning to clone people is okay.					
4. Using therapeutic cloning to clone an embryo in order to get embryonic stem cells to give to a person with damaged tissue, organs, or a certain disease is okay.					
5. Using therapeutic cloning to clone cells in order to study how diseased cells grow is okay.					
6. Using adult stem cells to give to people with damaged tissue, organs, or a certain disease is okay.					
7. Using embryonic stem cells from leftover embryos at IVF clinics in order to give to people with damaged tissue, organs, or a certain disease is okay.					

Statement	Number of students who feel this way				
	Strongly agree	Agree	Unsure	Disagree	Strongly disagree
8. The government should give money to scientists for embryonic stem cell research.					
9. The government should have laws regulating cloning and stem cells.					

Data from Cloning and Stem Cell Survey

Sheet B

Directions: Using the data collected from Sheet A, determine what **percent** of the students are in each category. To do this, divide each number on *Sheet A* by the total number of students in the class.

Number of students in this class: _____

Statement	Percent of students who feel this way				
	Strongly agree	Agree	Unsure	Disagree	Strongly disagree
1. Using reproductive cloning to clone a person's pet is okay.	%	%	%	%	%
2. Using reproductive cloning to clone endangered or extinct species is okay.	%	%	%	%	%
3. Using reproductive cloning to clone people is okay.	%	%	%	%	%
4. Using therapeutic cloning to clone an embryo in order to get embryonic stem cells to give to a person with damaged tissue, organs, or a certain disease is okay.	%	%	%	%	%
5. Using therapeutic cloning to clone cells in order to study how diseased cells grow is okay.	%	%	%	%	%
6. Using adult stem cells to give to people with damaged tissue, organ, or a certain disease is okay.	%	%	%	%	%
7. Using embryonic stem cells from leftover embryos at IVF clinics in order to give to people with damaged tissue, organs, or a certain disease is okay.	%	%	%	%	%

Statement	Percent of students who feel this way				
	Strongly agree	Agree	Unsure	Disagree	Strongly disagree
8. The government should give money to scientists for embryonic stem cell research.	%	%	%	%	%
9. The government should have laws regulating cloning and stem cells.	%	%	%	%	%

Sheet C

Part 2 (b): Data collection

Directions: Add up the total *number* of students for each statement that belong in each category (i.e., Strongly agree, Agree, etc.) and write each number in its respective category.

Number of students in this class: _____

Statement	Number of students who feel this way				
1. Using reproductive cloning to clone a person's pet is okay.	Strongly agree	Agree	Unsure	Disagree	Strongly disagree
Entire class					
Females					
Males					
People with pets					
People without pets					
2. Using reproductive cloning to clone endangered or extinct species is okay.	Strongly agree	Agree	Unsure	Disagree	Strongly disagree
Entire class					
Females					
Males					
People with pets					
People without pets					
3. Using reproductive cloning to clone people is okay.	Strongly agree	Agree	Unsure	Disagree	Strongly disagree
Entire class					
Females					
Males					
People with medical issues ("Medical issues" refers to people who know others with medical issues and/or have medical issues themselves.)					

Print This

3. Using reproductive cloning to clone people is okay.	Strongly agree	Agree	Unsure	Disagree	Strongly disagree
People with no medical issues ("No medical issues" refers to people who do not know others with medical issues and/or have no medical issues themselves.)					

4. Using therapeutic cloning to clone an embryo in order to get embryonic stem cells to give to a person with damaged tissue, organ, or a certain disease is okay.	Strongly agree	Agree	Unsure	Disagree	Strongly disagree
Entire class					
Females					
Males					
People with medical issues					
People with no medical issues					

5. Using therapeutic cloning to clone cells in order to study how diseased cells grow is okay.	Strongly agree	Agree	Unsure	Disagree	Strongly agree
Entire class					
Females					
Males					
People with medical issues					
People with no medical issues					

6. Using adult stem cells to give to people with damaged tissue, organs, or a certain disease is okay.	Strongly agree	Agree	Unsure	Disagree	Strongly agree
Entire class					
Females					
Males					
People with medical issues					
People with no medical issues					

7. Using embryonic stem cells from leftover embryos at IVF clinics in order to give to people with damaged tissue, organs, or a certain disease is okay.	Strongly agree	Agree	Unsure	Disagree	Strongly agree
Entire class					
Females					
Males					
People with medical issues					
People with no medical issues					
8. The government should give money to scientists for embryonic stem cell research.	Strongly agree	Agree	Unsure	Disagree	Strongly agree
Entire class					
Females					
Males					
People with medical issues					
People with no medical issues					
9. The government should have laws regulating cloning and stem cells.	Strongly agree	Agree	Unsure	Disagree	Strongly agree
Entire class					
Females					
Males					
People with pets					
People without pets					

Biotechnology: With Student Activities

Data from Cloning and Stem Cell Survey

Sheet D

Directions: Using the data collected from Sheet C, determine what **percent** of the students are in each category. To do this, divide each number on *Sheet C* by the total number of students in the class.

Number of students in this class: _____

Statement	Percent of students who feel this way				
1. Using reproductive cloning to clone a person's pet is okay.	Strongly agree	Agree	Unsure	Disagree	Strongly agree
Entire class	%	%	%	%	%
Females	%	%	%	%	%
Males	%	%	%	%	%
People with pets	%	%	%	%	%
People without pets	%	%	%	%	%
2. Using reproductive cloning to clone endangered or extinct species is okay.	Strongly agree	Agree	Unsure	Disagree	Strongly agree
Entire class	%	%	%	%	%
Females	%	%	%	%	%
Males	%	%	%	%	%
People with pets	%	%	%	%	%
People without pets	%	%	%	%	%
3. Using reproductive cloning to clone people is okay.	Strongly agree	Agree	Unsure	Disagree	Strongly agree
Entire class	%	%	%	%	%
Females	%	%	%	%	%
Males	%	%	%	%	%
Medical issues	%	%	%	%	%
No medical issues	%	%	%	%	%

4. Using therapeutic cloning to clone an embryo in order to get embryonic stem cells to give to a person with damaged tissue, organ, or a certain disease is okay.	Strongly agree	Agree	Unsure	Disagree	Strongly agree
Entire class	%	%	%	%	%
Females	%	%	%	%	%
Males	%	%	%	%	%
People with medical issues	%	%	%	%	%
People with no medical issues	%	%	%	%	%
5. Using therapeutic cloning to clone cells in order to study how diseased cells grow is okay.	Strongly agree	Agree	Unsure	Disagree	Strongly agree
Entire class	%	%	%	%	%
Females	%	%	%	%	%
Males	%	%	%	%	%
People with medical issues	%	%	%	%	%
People with no medical issues	%	%	%	%	%
6. Using adult stem cells to give to people with damaged tissue, organ, or a certain disease is okay.	Strongly agree	Agree	Unsure	Disagree	Strongly agree
Entire class	%	%	%	%	%
Females	%	%	%	%	%
Males	%	%	%	%	%
People with medical issues	%	%	%	%	%
People with no medical issues	%	%	%	%	%

7. Using embryonic stem cells from leftover embryos at IVF clinics in order to give to people with damaged tissue, organs, or a certain disease is okay.	Strongly agree	Agree	Unsure	Disagree	Strongly agree
Entire class	%	%	%	%	%
Females	%	%	%	%	%
Males	%	%	%	%	%
People with medical issues	%	%	%	%	%
People with no medical issues	%	%	%	%	%

8. The government should give money to scientists for embryonic stem cell research.	Strongly agree	Agree	Unsure	Disagree	Strongly agree
Entire class	%	%	%	%	%
Females	%	%	%	%	%
Males	%	%	%	%	%
People with medical issues	%	%	%	%	%
People with no medical issues	%	%	%	%	%

9. The government should have laws regulating cloning and stem cells.	Strongly agree	Agree	Unsure	Disagree	Strongly agree
Entire class	%	%	%	%	%
Females	%	%	%	%	%
Males	%	%	%	%	%
People with pets	%	%	%	%	%
People without pets	%	%	%	%	%
People with medical issues	%	%	%	%	%
People with no medical issues	%	%	%	%	%

Part 3 (a): Graphing the information

If you collected the information on Sheets A and B:

Either individually or with a partner/group, draw a bar graph for each of the nine statements about cloning and stem cell research. Place all graphs on a poster and include the answers to the analysis questions (*Part 4*) as well.

Example:

Class attitudes about the following statement: "Using reproductive cloning to clone a person's pet is okay."

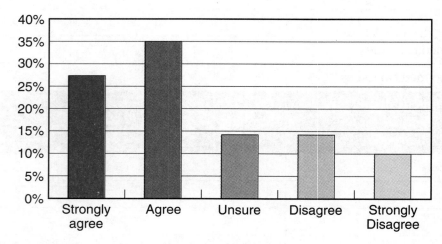

For an additional visual representation of the data, draw a pie graph for each statement by converting the percents to degrees. For example, for the first statement, if 27% of the class said "Strongly agree," multiply 27% (.27) by 360° to determine what angle to draw for that portion of the graph.

Class attitudes about the following statement:

"Using reproductive cloning to clone a person's pet is okay."

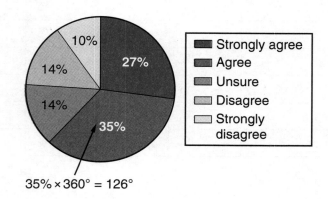

Part 3 (b): Graphing the information

If you collected the information on Sheets C and D:

Either individually or with a partner/group, draw three to four bar graphs for each of the nine statements about cloning and stem cell research. For example, for the first statement ("Using reproductive cloning to clone a person's pet is okay") create one graph showing the results for the entire class, one comparing males and females, and one comparing people with and without pets. Place all graphs on a poster and include the answers to the analysis questions as well.

Example:

Class attitudes about the following statement:

"Using reproductive cloning to clone a person's pet is okay."

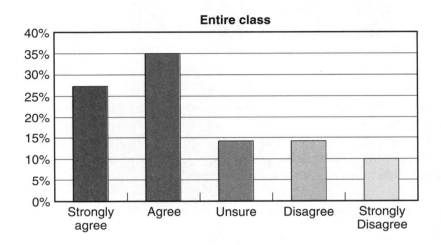

Class attitudes about the following statement:

"Using reproductive cloning to clone a person's pet is okay."

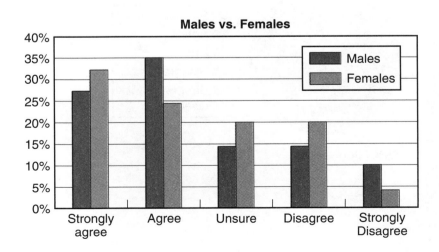

Class attitudes about the following statement:

"*Using reproductive cloning to clone a person's pet is okay.*"

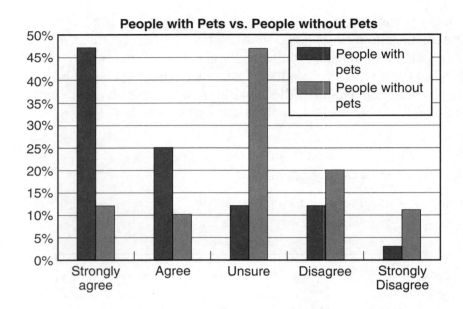

People with Pets vs. People without Pets

For an additional visual representation of the data, draw a pie graph for each statement by converting the percents to degrees. For example, for the first statement, if 35% of the class said "Agree," multiply 35% (.35) by 360° to determine what angle to draw for that portion of the graph. *Note:* It is best to create a pie graph for only the **entire class** results of each statement.

Class attitudes about the following statement:

"*Using reproductive cloning to clone a person's pet is okay.*"

Entire class

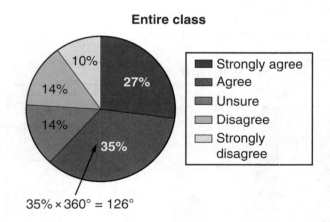

$35\% \times 360° = 126°$

Part 4 (a): Analyzing the information

Answer these questions if you collected data on Sheets A and B.

1. What conclusions can you draw about how the class feels about the use of reproductive cloning on animals (both pets and endangered/extinct animals) and on people?
2. What conclusions can you make about how the class feels about therapeutic stem cell use *vs.* adult stem cell use?
3. What conclusions can you make about how the class feels about using stem cells that were left over from IVF clinics to do therapeutic stem cell research?
4. What conclusions can you make about how the class feels about the government having laws about and giving money to stem cell research?
5. If you were to add questions to this survey regarding people's views of cloning and stem cell research, what other information would you want to know? How could this information be helpful?

Part 4 (b): Analyzing the information

Answer these questions if you collected data on Sheets C and D.

To analyze the information for the entire class, answer questions 1–5 above; then answer the following two questions.

1. (a) What differences, if any, can you see between the opinions of males *vs.* females regarding cloning and stem cell research?
   (b) What differences, if any, can you see between the opinions of people who have pets vs. people who do not have pets regarding cloning animals?
   (c) Speculate why there are these differences in opinion (or why there is no difference in opinion, if that is the case).

2. (a) What differences, if any, can you see between the opinions of people who have a medical condition (or know someone with a medical condition) *vs.* people who do not have a medical condition (or do not know someone with a medical condition) regarding therapeutic cloning and stem cell research?
   (b) Speculate why there are these differences in opinion (or why there is no difference in opinion, if that is the case).

Vocabulary Crossword

Directions: *Each clue below is a definition of one of the vocabulary words that you learned in this chapter. On a printout of this page provided by your teacher, write the word that matches each definition inside the numbered vertical or horizontal spaces. All the vocabulary words from Chapter 6 are used in this puzzle.*

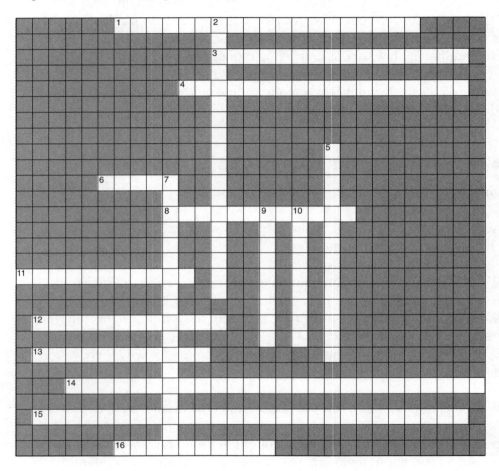

Across

1. Cloning a whole individual
3. Cells with a specific job to do
4. Cloning certain cells of an organism
6. An organism (or part of an organism) that is the exact genetic match of another organism
8. Variety of traits within and between species
11. Describes a cell that has the ability to turn into many of the cells that make up an organism
12. Involves determining if something is morally right or wrong, and does not always have a clear right or wrong answer
13. Any body cell in an organism other than a sperm cell or an egg cell
14. The process of transferring the nucleus from a somatic cell of the organism to be cloned into an enucleated egg cell
15. A type of stem cell that appears to be similar to embryonic stem cells and is made by "reprogramming" certain cells in the body to turn on the genes that let cells be flexible
16. An embryo in the early stages of development that is made up of a ball of 150 cells

Down

2. Cells that do not have a specific job to do
5. Unspecialized cells that are found in certain parts of the body and are used to maintain and repair the tissue in which they are found
7. Unspecialized cells from an embryo that are used to turn into most of the cell types of an organism
9. To remove the nucleus from a cell
10. Cells that can grow copies of themselves indefinitely and then can turn into other types of cell

212   Biotechnology: With Student Activities

Multiple Choice

For each question, choose the letter of the answer choice that best completes the sentence or answers the question.

1. An example of a specialized cell is a(n)
   a. embryonic stem cell
   b. adult stem cell
   c. islet (pancreatic) cell
   d. pluripotent stem cell

2. There are _____ embryonic stem cells in an adult person.
   a. zero   b. 150   c. 250   d. 1000

3. Adult stem cells have so far been found in _____ part(s) of the body
   a. every   b. certain   c. one   d. no

4. Embryonic stem cells can develop into
   a. muscle cells   b. heart cells   c. nerve cells   d. all of these cells

5. The experiments using embryonic stem cells on mice have been
   a. disastrous
   b. successful
   c. unsuccessful
   d. inconclusive

6. Scientists' cloning of a whole person has _____ been done.
   a. never   b. rarely   c. sometimes   d. often

7. _____ are an example of clones that occur naturally.
   a. Fraternal twins
   b. Identical twins
   c. All brothers
   d. All sisters

8. An enucleated cell has had its nucleus
   a. added   b. removed   c. doubled   d. cut in half

9. To clone an organism, scientists need a _____ cell from that organism.
   a. large   b. reproductive   c. somatic   d. sperm

10. Therapeutic cloning is used to make
    a. sheep   b. cows   c. tomatoes   d. certain cells or tissues

11. Religious groups have _____ views on stem cell research and cloning.
    a. comparable   b. similar   c. different   d. no official

12. Most scientists have _____ desire to clone a whole person.
    a. no   b. a little   c. some   d. much

13. Some people are concerned that cloned animals are more susceptible to
    a. early death   b. health problems   c. infections   d. all of the above

---

14. The use of embryonic stem cells is very
    a. popular   b. accepted   c. controversial   d. widespread

15. Currently, in some countries, embryonic stem cell research is
    a. outlawed   b. unethical   c. very inexpensive   d. regulated by laws

True or False

Read each statement and indicate whether it is true or false. If it is false, correct the underlined word(s) to make the statement true.

1. There are about <u>75 types</u> of cells in the human body.   1. _____

2. Scientists hope to one day use stem cells to treat people with <u>damaged heart tissue</u>.   2. _____

3. Embryonic stem cells are <u>less</u> versatile than adult stem cells.   3. _____

4. Embryonic stem cells come from a <u>blastocyst</u>.   4. _____

5. Induced pluripotent stem cells seem to be similar to <u>adult stem cells</u>.   5. _____

6. An example of a somatic cell is <u>an egg cell</u>.   6. _____

7. The first time a mammal was cloned from an adult cell was in <u>1996</u>.   7. _____

8. A <u>sheep</u> was the first mammal to be cloned from an adult cell.   8. _____

9. <u>Reproductive cloning</u> is used to clone cells or tissue.   9. _____

10. <u>Therapeutic cloning</u> requires the use of a surrogate mother.   10. _____

11. In some states, breaking the cloning laws can result in <u>fines and/or prison time</u>.   11. _____

12. Stem cell research has <u>no</u> federal funding available for it.   12. _____

13. <u>All 50</u> states in the U.S. have laws about cloning.   13. _____

14. <u>Adult stem cells</u> are taken from leftover embryos at IVF clinics.   14. _____

15. Cloned animals probably <u>do not always</u> have the same behavior as the animal they were cloned from.   15. _____

Short Answer

Answer the following questions in one or two complete sentences.

1. Describe *three* reasons why scientists are interested in doing stem cell research.
2. Explain why scientists are more interested in using embryonic stem cells than adult stem cells.
3. Identify where scientists get the embryos from for stem cell research.
4. Explain why there is interest in the creation of induced pluripotent stem cells and why this might ease some people's concerns about stem cell research.
5. Explain, in *five* steps, how a scientist would use somatic cell nuclear transfer to create tissue that was an exact genetic match for a patient.
6. Justify why a cloned person (produced by scientists from an adult cell) could not be the same age as the person from whom he/she was cloned.
7. What can you infer about the DNA of a cloned animal and the animal from which it was cloned?
8. Imagine that a scientist was trying to clone a whole dog; explain why three dogs are needed to carry out this process.
9. Explain why using embryonic stem cells is so controversial.
10. What are the reasons why some people support stem cell research?
11. What are concerns some people have about cloning a whole person?
12. (a) Describe the federal law regarding embryonic stem cell research before March 9, 2009. (b) Explain how the law changed after that date.

Going Further

Based on the information in this chapter and the list of pros and cons that you wrote for Lesson 6.3 Review, decide how you feel about cloning and stem cell research. Do you feel these types of biotechnology could be helpful to people or do you feel scientists should not be doing such research? Pick one of the two technologies and write an essay in which you defend your opinion; use information from the chapter as well as your own personal beliefs. If you pick stem cells, make sure to differentiate between adult and embryonic stem cells. If you pick cloning, make sure to differentiate between therapeutic and reproductive cloning. You should also include a brief summary of what the procedure involves. Your essay will be graded according to the rubric provided by your teacher.

Glossary

Glossary

A

adult stem cells unspecialized cells that are found in certain parts of an organism's body; they are used to maintain and repair the tissue in which they are found

allele variations of a gene; in sexual reproduction, organisms inherit two alleles (at least) for every trait, one from each parent

amino acids the substances that link together to build proteins; each codon calls for a specific amino acid

antibiotic a substance that kills the bacteria that can make people sick

autosomal dominant disorder describes a genetic disorder that is caused by inheriting just one dominant allele

autosomal recessive disorder describes a genetic disorder that is caused by inheriting the recessive alleles

B

bacteria microorganisms that have only one cell; some are helpful, some are harmful

base pairs held together by chemical (hydrogen) bonds, the DNA nitrogen base pairs are adenine with thymine and cytosine with guanine

behavioral traits describes how an organism acts (such as its aggressiveness, level of energy, hunting ability, type of movement)

biodiversity the variety of traits within and between species, and the variety of species within ecosystems

biofuels renewable resources such as plants that can be used for energy sources

bioreactor a machine that provides the ideal temperature and nutrients to allow the genetically engineered bacteria to grow and multiply many times

bioremediation using living things, such as bacteria, to help fix a problem, specifically to clean up an environmental problem such as an oil spill

biotechnology companies businesses in which scientists use their knowledge of DNA to research genetic diseases and try to develop medications to treat people who suffer from the disorders

biotechnology the science of using or changing living things to improve or benefit peoples' lives

blastocyst the term for a mammal's embryo in its early stages of development; a ball of 150 cells that contains an inner cell mass of stem cells

browns organic materials that are high in carbohydrates and provide the element carbon; include such things as autumn leaves, straw, and paper products

C

carriers describes people who have one allele for a disease but who do not have the disease; that is, they have one dominant and one recessive allele

chromosomes inside the nucleus, the long strands of DNA that are twisted and coiled

clone an organism, or part of an organism, that is the exact genetic match of another organism

codons the groups of three bases, or triplet codes, by which the cell reads the DNA

compost the product of decomposition of organic material; a dark brown, nutrient-rich material; see *humus*

composting a process that speeds up the decomposition of organic matter by providing the ideal conditions for it

D

***Deepwater Horizon* oil spill** the largest accidental ocean oil spill to date; occurred in Gulf of Mexico in April 2010

deletion a mutation in which one or more bases are removed from the DNA

deoxyribose the five-carbon sugar that makes up part of the sides of the DNA "ladder"

designer baby a human baby that has had his or her genes artificially selected for by scientists

direct gene transfer in vivo technique in which vectors are used to transport the functioning gene directly into a person's body

DNA deoxyribonucleic acid; the molecule that contains the instructions for making an organism

DNA replication process by which the DNA molecule unwinds, opens up like a zipper, and then makes two identical strands to the original ones

DNA sequencing the process researchers carry out to determine the order of DNA nitrogen bases in samples from people; they can compare the DNA sequences to find differences between them, and then see if those differences are the genes that cause a genetic disease

dominant allele the trait that shows; will block expression of the other allele

double helix shape that resembles two lines twisted around a central axis

E

E85 an ethanol-gasoline fuel mixture that consists of 85% ethanol and 15% gasoline

embryo an organism in the early stages of development that is formed after a fertilized egg starts to divide (and then differentiate)

embryonic stem cells the unspecialized cells in an embryo that differentiate into most cell types of an organism

enucleate in cloning process, means to remove the nucleus from a somatic or egg cell

environmental mutations mutations that are developed during a person's lifetime and which are not inherited

enzyme a protein found in an organism that can affect chemical reactions

ethanol a clear, colorless, non-toxic liquid fuel that is made from the sugars in plants

ethical issue involves determining if something is morally right or wrong, such as cloning organisms

eugenics the thought some people once had that certain physical and mental traits were more desirable than others

***Exxon Valdez* oil spill** large oil spill that occurred off the coast of Alaska in March 1989

F

fermentation the process by which yeast cells eat sugars in plants and produce the waste gas carbon dioxide; and by which yeast also produces liquid ethanol

fertilization the moment when the heredity material from the egg cell and sperm cell combine to create a new organism

Flexible Fuel Vehicles (FFVs) the type of car needed to use E85 fuel; can run on regular gasoline or on a combination of ethanol and gasoline

fossil fuel a fuel made from the fossilized remains of ancient plants and animals

frame-shift mutation mutations in which there is either an insertion or a deletion, and the other bases have to move over to fill in the gap or to make room for bases

G

gene gun a machine that shoots gene-coated pellets through the cells of a crop plant in order to introduce a new gene to that plant

gene splicing the process of joining one section of DNA with another; done with use of a vector

gene therapy a technique that aims to fix the mutations in a person's DNA that cause a genetic disease; the normal DNA is given to do the work of the defective DNA

genes the instructions for all traits that organisms pass on to their offspring; sections of DNA

genetic discrimination when people are treated unfairly because of some trait they may have, which may be known about due to the results of a genetic test; e.g., if people undergo genetic testing and discover that they are likely to develop a genetic disease, employers might not want to hire them and health insurance companies might not want to insure them

genetic disease condition that is caused by a mutation in an organism's DNA; it can be inherited

genetic engineering the process of changing an organism's DNA by adding or removing sections of DNA or by turning genes "on" or "off" in an organism

genetic testing procedure by which scientists examine people's DNA to find out if they are carriers of any genetic diseases or if they have a genetic disease

genetically modified (GM) foods crops and animals that have had their DNA changed by scientists, usually for better growth and/or nutrition

genetics the study of how our traits are passed from one generation to the next

genome for a person or population, all of the DNA, which includes all the genes

genotypes the combinations of dominant and recessive alleles for traits

germ-line mutations mutations that are passed from one generation to the next

greens organic materials that are high in protein and provide the element nitrogen; include such things as grass clippings and food scraps (egg shells, apple cores)

H

helix shape that resembles a line that is twisted around a central axis

herbicides chemicals that are used to kill weeds that can harm crops, but can also hurt all plants

heredity the passing of traits from one generation to the next

human growth hormone (hGH) the protein that controls growth in the human body and is secreted from the pituitary gland in the brain

human insulin a protein that is produced by the pancreas gland after a person has eaten and the body experiences high levels of glucose in the blood.

humus the product of decomposition of organic material; a dark brown, nutrient-rich material; see *compost*

I

identical twins develop when a fertilized egg splits in two, creating two separate organisms that have the same DNA

induced pluripotent stem cells human cells that are similar to embryonic stem cells and which are thought to have the ability to turn into many different cell types

insecticides types of pesticides, the chemicals that can kill insects; can be dangerous to handle

insertion a mutation in which one or more bases are inserted into the DNA

inversion a mutation in which a section of the DNA is reversed

in vitro a Latin term that means "in glass"; refers to when scientists carry out a procedure in a test tube or petri dish

in vivo a Latin term that means "in the living"; refers to when scientists carry out a procedure directly in the body

M

microorganism very small living thing that can be viewed only with a microscope

mold a microorganism that, like yeast, is a type of fungus; usually black, blue, or green

mutagens factors that can lead to environmental mutations, such as radiation and certain chemicals

mutation a mistake in the DNA which could result in a trait that is not normal or common; can result in a disease or a disorder

N

nitrogen bases the four substances that make up the "rungs" of the DNA "ladder"; adenine, thymine, cytosine, and guanine

nucleotide subunits the four nitrogen bases along with the phosphate and five-carbon sugar molecules that make up the DNA molecule

nucleus the central part of a cell where the instructions (DNA) for the cell's functioning are located

O

offspring refers to the one or more organisms that are produced by reproduction

organic something living or that comes from a living thing; eventually decomposes

organism word used to refer to any living thing

P

penicillin medicinal bacteria-killing substance from the *Penicillium* mold

phenotype the way the genotype expresses itself as an observable trait in the offspring

physical traits describes how an organism looks (such as its size, shape, color of fur)

plasmid the loop of DNA separate from the bacterium's main DNA; used for genetic engineering since scientists can cut open the loop and paste in the new gene

point mutation a mutation in which one nitrogen base has been replaced by another nitrogen base

polymorphisms slight changes that develop in the DNA and result in differences in traits within a species

pre-implantation genetic diagnosis (PGD) the process by which scientists look for embryos that have certain desired traits and implant only those embryos into a woman's womb

proteins large, chainlike molecules of amino acids that form the building blocks of cells and make up the hormones and enzymes that keep our bodies functioning

Punnett square is a chart that shows the possible combinations of alleles that could be created during fertilization

R

recessive allele the trait that can be blocked by the dominant allele

recombinant DNA the new DNA that is created from gene splicing

renewable resources energy sources that have the ability to renew themselves

rennin enzyme from the lining of animal stomachs that can turn milk into cheese

reproductive cells the cells that pass on the genetic information to the offspring; i.e., the egg cells and sperm cells

reproductive cloning the process by which scientists use cloning to produce a whole individual organism

restriction enzymes proteins that will cut the DNA at very specific places

S

selective breeding the process by which two organisms with desirable traits are bred to produce offspring with those same desired traits

sexual reproduction describes when a living thing is produced by the joining up of heredity material from two parents

somatic cell any cell in an organism other than a sperm or egg cell; that is, a body cell

somatic cell nuclear transfer the process of transferring the nucleus from a somatic cell (of the organism to be cloned) into an enucleated egg cell

specialized cells the cells in an embryo as it develops; that is, the cells that change and have specific jobs

stem cells the unspecialized cells that make up the embryo in its early stages of development

sugar-phosphate backbone provides support for the (sides of the) DNA molecule

T

therapeutic cloning the process by which scientists use cloning only to produce certain cells or tissues of an organism

transgenic organism one that has had genes from a different kind of organism transferred into its DNA

U

undifferentiated cells those which have not yet become specialized; used in modified DNA procedures (to accept new genes)

unspecialized cells all the cells in an early embryo; the cells are still the same and they do not have any specific jobs to do

V

vector a bacterial plasmid or virus into which the new gene is spliced for transport

Y

yeast a microorganism that is a type of fungus; found in the air and in the ground

Index

Index

A

ADA (adenosine deaminase) deficiency, 152
Adenine, 76
Adult-onset diabetes, 146
Adult stem cells, 177–78
Advanced Cell Technology (biotechnology company), 188–89
Agricultural biotechnology, 156
Agrobacterium tumefaciens, 158
Albinism, 102
Alleles
    defined, 110
    dominant, 110–12
    recessive, 110–12
Alzheimer's disease, 116, 121, 176
Amino acids, 79, 81
    identifying with codon wheel, 91–93
Amino acid sequence of insulin, 95
Anemia, sickle-cell, 117
Antibiotics, 12
Archaeologists, 6, 9
Artifacts, 6
Autosomal recessive disorders, 116–17
    defined, 117–18
Avery, Oswald, 66

B

Bacillus thuringiensis (BT), 157
Bacteria, 6
    in making medicine, 146–48
    oil-eating, 44
Baker's yeast, 9
Base pairs, 76
Behavioral traits, 15, 25
Biodiversity, 189
Biofuels, 35
Bioreactor, 147
Bioremediation, 42–44
    defined, 43
    effect of temperature on, 55–56
    steps of, 57
Biotechnology
    agricultural, 156
    bread-making as, 9–10
    cheese-making as, 6

classical, 146
defined, 2–3
examples of, 4
modern, 146
penicillin development as example of, 12–13
selective breeding as example of, 15–16, 24–29
Biotechnology companies, 121–22
Blastocyst, 177
Boyer, Herbert, 141, 146, 147, 150
Bread-making, 9–10
    as biotechnology, 9–10
Breeding, selective, 15–16, 24–29
Browns, 47
Bt corn, 157

C

Cancer, 103
Carriers, 111–12
Cells
    egg, 71
    germ, 103
    reproductive, 71, 103
    sex, 103
    somatic, 182
    specialized, 176
    sperm, 71
    stem, 4
    undifferentiated, 158
    unspecialized, 176
Chain, Ernst, 12, 13
Cheese-making, as biotechnology, 6
Chromosomes, 75
    sex, 76
Classical biotechnology, 146
Clone, 182
Cloning, 4, 182–85
    future of, 191
    reproductive, 182–85
    therapeutic, 182
Codons
    defined, 80
    start, 80
    stop, 80–81

Cohen, Stanley, 141, 146, 150
Combination, 142
Composting, 48
   as beneficial process, 47–49
   defined, 47
Contagious diseases, 116
Crick, Francis, 67, 76
Cystic fibrosis, 117
Cytosine, 76

D

Data, comparing, on genetically modified
   crops, 168–69
Decomposers, 47
Deepwater Horizon oil spill, 42, 44, 52
Deletion, 107
Deoxyribose, 76
Designer baby, 162–64
De Silva, Ashanti, 152
Diabetes, 146, 176
   adult-onset, 146
   juvenile, 146
Direct gene transfer, 151
DNA (deoxyribonucleic acid), 4
   discovery of, 65–67
   function of, 79–81
   making model of, 85–87
   purpose of, 70–72
   replication of, 79
   sequencing, 121–22
   structure of, 66, 75–76
Dolly (cloned sheep), 183, 189
Dominant allele, 110–12
Dominate genes, 65
Double helix, 67, 76
Down syndrome, 116
Dwarfism, 102

E

E10, 36
E85
   defined, 36
   in reducing use of fossil fuels, 35–36
Egg cells, 71
Embryo, 162
Embryonic stem cells, 176–77
   research on, 188
Engineering, genetic, 163–64
Enuncleate, 182

Environmental mutations, 103
Enviropig, 158
Enzymes
   defined, 6
   restriction, 141
Escherichia coli, 146, 158
Ethanol
   defined, 35
   in reducing use of fossil fuels, 35–36
Ethical issues, 122, 188–91
Eugenics, 164
Exxon Valdez oil spill, 42, 44, 52

F

Fermentation, 11
   defined, 10, 19, 35
Fertilization
   defined, 71
   in vitro, 162, 177
Flavr Savr tomato, 156
Fleming, Alexander, 12, 13
Flexible Fuel Vehicles, 36
Florey, Howard, 12, 13
Flour, 9
Foods, genetically modified, 156–59,
   168–69
Ford, Henry, 36
Fossil fuels, reducing use of, 35–36
Frame-shift mutations, 108
Franklin, Rosalind, 66–67
Fraternal twins, 71–72
Fungus, 9

G

Gene gun, 158
Genentech (biotechnology company),
   147, 150
Genes, 15
   dominate, 65
   recessive, 65
Gene splicing, 142
Gene therapy, 122, 151–53
   benefits of, 151
   defined, 151
   in vitro, 151–52
   in vivo, 151
Genetically engineering, 148
Genetically modified (GM) foods, 156–59,
   168–69

Genetic code, 80, 88–90
Genetic discrimination, 122
Genetic diseases, 151
  defined, 116
  types of, 116–18
Genetic engineering, 4, 141–43, 163–64
  defined, 141
Genetic engineers, 141
Genetic Information Nondiscrimination
  Act (2008), 122
Genetic mutations, 116, 177
  causes of, 102–4
Genetics, 65
Genetic testing, 121
Genome, 70
Genotypes, 110
Germ cells, 103
Germ-line mutations, 103
Glucose, 146
Golden Rice, 157
Greens, 47
Griffith, Frederick, 65–66
Guanine, 76

H

Heart disease, 176
Helix shape, 67
Herbicides, 157
Heredity, 71–72
  defined, 71–72
Human Genome Project, 100
Human growth hormone (hGH), 148
Human insulin, 146
Humus, 48
Huntington's disease, 116, 118, 121
Hybrid, 29
Hypothermia, 43
Hypothesis, 20

I

Identical twins, 71, 182
Induced pluripotent stem cells, 178
Insecticides, 157
Insertion, 107–8
Insulin
  amino acid sequence of, 95
  human, 146
Inversion, 107
In vitro, 151

In vitro fertilization (IVF), 162, 177
In vitro gene therapy, 151–52
In vivo, 151
In vivo gene therapy, 151

J

Juvenile diabetes, 146

M

Medicine, bacteria in making, 146–48
Mendel, Gregor, 65
Mice, effect of penicillin on, 22
Microbes, 44
Microorganisms, 3
Microscope, 3
Modern biotechnology, 146
Mold, 12
Moral concerns, 122
Mutagens, 103
Mutations, 116
  defined, 102
  environmental, 103
  frame-shift, 108
  genetic, 102–4, 116, 177
  germ-line, 103
  point, 107
  types of, 107–8

N

Nature, 189
Nitrogen, 47
Nitrogen bases, 76
Nucleotide subunits, 76
Nucleus, 75
Nurture, 189

O

Offspring, 15
Oil-eating bacteria, 44
Oil spills, 43
  Deepwater Horizon, 42, 44, 52
  Exxon Valdez, 42, 44, 52
  simulation of, 52–54
Organic material, 47–49
Organism, 3
  transgenic, 142–43

Photo Credits

Chapter 1
Page 1: Flock of sheep and goats in Mideast, Getty Images/Alistair Duncan
Page 6: Swiss cheese, iStockphoto/Gabor Izso
Page 9 (*left*): Middle Eastern flatbreads, iStockphoto/Krishna Kumar
Page 9 (*right*): Yeast cells, Science Photo Library/Steve Gschmeissner/Corbis
Page 15: Yorkshire terriers, Meghan J. Shupe
Page 16: Several apple varieties, iStockphoto/Craftvision

Chapter 2
Page 34: Rescued sea duck, coastal oil spill, Getty Images/Ben Osborne
Page 35: Cornfield in Mississippi, Getty Images/Joanna McCarthy
Page 42: Oil spill (from *Deepwater Horizon*), Gulf of Mexico, NASA Images
Page 43: Rescued sea duck, coastal oil spill, Getty Images/Ben Osborne
Page 47: Banana peels, apple cores, egg shells, Meghan J. Shupe
Page 48 (*top*): Large compost pile, iStockphoto/PinkBadger
Page 48 (*bottom*): Shovelful of humus, iStockphoto/Sebastien Cote

Chapter 3
Page 64: Human chromosomes, Photo Researchers/Biophoto Associates
Page 65: Garden pea plant, Photo Researchers/Alan & Linda Detrick
Page 66: X-ray photograph of a DNA molecule, Photo Researchers/Rosalind Franklin/ Omikron
Page 67: Watson and Crick with DNA model, Photo Researchers/A. Barrington Brown
Page 70 (*left*): Teenagers with laptop computer, Reggie Casagrande
Page 70 (*right*): Young chimp walking upright, Photo Researchers/Tim Davis
Page 71 (*left*): Human egg and sperm cells (fertilization), Getty Images
Page 71 (*right*): Teenage identical twin sisters, Science Photo Library/Ian Hooton
Page 72 (*left*): Young fraternal twin brothers, Todd Warnock/Taxi
Page 72 (*right*): Scientists examining DNA patterns, Visuals Unlimited, Inc., © SIU
Page 75: Human chromosome, Photo Researchers/Biophoto Associates

Chapter 4
Page 101: Scientists at microscope, iStockphoto/Alexander Raths
Page 103: X-ray of human hand, Photo Researchers/Biophoto Associates
Page 104: Height range among men, N.Y. Public Library/Science, Industry, and Business Library
Page 116: Sickle cell and normal red blood cells, Photo Researchers/Meckes/Ottawa
Page 117: Set of human chromosomes with extra chromosome number 21, Photo Researchers/Biophoto Associates
Page 121 (*top*): Scientists at microscope, iStockphoto/Alexander Raths
Page 121 (*bottom*): Newborn babies, Photo Researchers/Catherine Ursillo
Page 122: Medicine bottles and prescription, Tetra Images/Corbis

Chapter 5

Page 140: Scissors cutting DNA (computer art), Photo Researchers/Laguna Design

Page 146: Genetically engineered *E. coli* bacteria, Science Photo Library/Volker Steger

Page 153: Treatment for cystic fibrosis patient, Photo Researchers/Hattie Young

Page 156 (*left*): Basket of groceries, Getty Images/Brand X Pictures

Page 156 (*right*): Scientist examining engineered tomatoes, Corbis

Page 157 (*top*): Worker spraying fields in California, Getty Images/Paul Grebliunas

Page 157 (*bottom*): Bananas growing on tree, Ocean/Corbis

Page 158: Gene gun being prepared to blast genes, Jim Richardson/Corbis

Page 159 (*top left*): Brazil nuts, Image Source/Corbis

Page 159 (*bottom left*): Soybeans and pea pods, Nugene Chiang/AsiaPix/Corbis

Page 159 (*right*): Monarch caterpillar on milkweed leaf, Getty Images/Ingo Arndt

Page 162: Ultrasonograph of a fetus, Photo Researchers/Doug Martin

Page 163: In vitro fertilization procedure, Matthew Polak/Sygma/Corbis

Page 164: "Doogie" mouse, Time & Life Pictures/Getty Images/Bill Ballenberg

Chapter 6

Page 175: Dolly, the first mammal cloned from an adult body cell, AP/Wide World Photos/John Chadwick

Page 184 (*left*): Dolly, cloned mammal, AP/Wide World Photos/John Chadwick

Page 184 (*right*): *Tyrannosaurus rex* illustration, Science Photo Library/Roger Harris

Page 188: Actor Christopher Reeve, Wally McNamee/Corbis

Page 189: Cheetah mother and cub, Lawson Wood/Corbis

Page 191: President Obama signing a law on stem cells, Shawn Thew/Corbis